# The Long Escape

# IRVING WERSTEIN

# The Long Escape

CHARLES SCRIBNER'S SONS

New York

This book is dedicated
to the memory of

# Captain John G. Sturges

my friend, a man of the sea,
who faced wind, storm and
torpedoes without flinching

# Contents

Prologue                                            9

Doomsday                                           29

Exodus                                             51

Dunkerque                                         135

MAPS                          *facing pages*    11, 31
AUTHOR'S NOTE                                     187

# Prologue

*"...war at best is barbarism..."*

War came to Belgium on May 10, 1940, a Friday. It came swiftly and without warning. Swarms of German bombing planes—*Heinkels* and *Stukas*—roared overhead, unleashing their tons of explosives on picture-postcard villages, on centuries-old cities, on railroads, freight yards and airfields. Death rained from the spring skies on that gentle Friday morning, a morning which had dawned with no hint or portent that anything unusual would happen.

War was German paratroopers, dropping from glider planes and seizing bridges, communication centers, crossroads and frontier posts. Everywhere on the Belgian-German border, cannon roared, tanks rolled and infantry marched. The coldly precise *Wehrmacht,* the German army, moved in its impersonal efficiency to overwhelm startled Belgian border guards.

The Germans had struck again at Belgium. As they had in the First World War, German jackboots thudded on the cobblestone streets of ancient Belgian cities. Places that had earned martyrdom in the

1914–18 war suffered new agonies after a respite of only twenty-six years.

From 1914 to 1918 the double-headed eagle flag of Imperial Germany had flown over Belgium; then the conquerors swore allegiance to their Kaiser, Wilhelm II. But in 1940 the Kaiser no longer ruled. Autocratic Germany, which had become a republic in 1919 after losing the war, turned away from democracy fourteen years later. The German Republic died in 1933 after more than a decade of continuous crisis.

The people chose an unlikely Messiah to lead them along paths of glory. The *Fuehrer*—the Leader —they called him. His name was Adolf Hitler. Austrian-born, Hitler had been an unsuccessful artist, an inept paper hanger, a World War I corporal and a dabbler in many causes.

Shortly after the end of the 1914–18 war this bitter and frustrated man helped organize the National Socialist German Workers' Party, a name soon shortened to Nazi. Hitler had a talent for rabble rousing and his speeches for the Nazi Party brought him to public attention. More and more people gathered in Munich beer halls to hear him speak against Germany's enemies—the Jews, the "international bankers," the communists, liberals, socialists and intellectuals (all of whom he lumped together) and the "decadent democracies" (England, France and the United States).

Hitler called upon his listeners to do away with the "infamous" Versailles Treaty which had ended World War I. He urged Germans to break with the past and to establish a New Order by putting the Nazi Party into power. He, Adolf Hitler, would lead Germany in a crusade. "I will make our Fatherland supreme!" he promised and coined the Nazi slogan: "Today Germany! Tomorrow the world!"

"*Heil Hitler!*" the audiences roared in cadenced chants. "*Sieg Heil!*" Hail Hitler! Hail Victory!

The echoes of their shouts reverberated in the great capitals of Europe. Men in London, Warsaw, Prague, Paris, Vienna, Moscow and Brussels—in cities, towns and hamlets—heard the turbulent outcry, the open threats, but paid them no heed. Across the Atlantic, Hitler's harsh voice reached American ears, but no one listened.

On the whole, the democracies saw Hitler as a comic figure with his toothbrush mustache, ill-fitting uniforms and ranting speeches. He seemed more a clown than a menace. But one day the world awoke, frightened and amazed. The *Fuehrer* was no buffoon; while free men napped, he had created the most powerful army and air force in history. Not since the time of Napoleon had such military might been gathered in one country.

German tanks—known as *panzers*—were juggernauts of destruction. German planes had no equal. The *Wehrmacht* was the best trained and equipped army anywhere. Hitler had forged a gigantic secret police organization—the *Gestapo*—in which every man was a master of terror and torture. His elite troops—the *Schutz-Staffeln* or *SS*—were comprised of dedicated Nazi fanatics.

And Hitler kept his word to the German masses. Anti-Nazis were hunted down. He imprisoned them in concentration camps, where they met torture or death. Thousands of his enemies fled their native land to wander as homeless exiles from place to place, haunted and hounded refugees whose harrowing tales shocked an incredulous world.

Still no one acted; only a few spoke out to stop the spread of Nazi tyranny. By the end of the 1930's it was too late. The rapacious Nazis swallowed the Ruhr Valley and the Saar Basin from which the Germans had been ejected after World War I. In 1938 they marched into Austria and occupied that country to force *anschluss*—a merger between the two teutonic nations, thus restoring a political alliance that had existed before the Great War of 1914–18. In 1938 Hitler also took over Czechoslovakia, a democracy established by the Versailles Treaty.

The New Order had come. The Nazis' *Swastika* flag fluttered over millions and the Nazi tyrant ruled his subjects with a barbarism unknown since the Dark Ages. But still his appetite remained unsated. He wanted more conquests. In September, 1939, he launched a ferocious attack on Poland, which resisted with futile valor.

The Poles, no matter how brave, could not withstand the Nazi onslaught alone. England and France, pledged to defend Polish sovereignty, had only one honorable course to follow. They reluctantly went to war against the Germans. British armies crossed the Channel to France and took up battle stations on the old fields of World War I.

The French marched into their Maginot Line, a series of fortifications that stretched along the German border all the way to the Swiss frontier. The Maginot Line symbolized for France the apex of military security. Its mammoth steel forts and huge guns were presumed to be impregnable. Never again would German soldiers ravage French soil as they had in the First World War.

Poland's armies were crushed in eighteen days, although sporadic fighting continued for another two weeks, especially around Warsaw. The country was viciously murdered by Nazi might in a technique known as *blitzkrieg* or lightning war which utilized *panzers* and air power. The German *Luftwaffe*—her air force—displayed tactics that made military observers gasp in awe. *Stuka* dive bombers acted as mobile artillery; the *panzers* tore through the Polish army like fleet cavalry.

Poland's agony soon ended in the field. But Hitler

had another surprise for the horrified world. He put into practice a policy of genocide—the mass destruction of all persons he considered undesirable —men, women and children. These included Jews, Poles, gypsies, anyone the *Fuehrer* deemed as "impure" or "non-Aryan." Those spared from slaughter he made German slaves; in the civilized twentieth century the ancient cruelty of forced labor had reappeared.

Shortly after the Poles had been crushed, Hitler called in his General Staff and demanded a plan of operations against France, whom he regarded as the "ultimate enemy." The Nazi generals drew up a blueprint called "Code Yellow." It outlined the swift, ruthless invasion of three neutral countries— Luxembourg, Holland and Belgium—to open the gateway into France by outflanking the Maginot Line.

The designers and builders of the Maginot Line had created a near masterpiece of military science but their brainchild was born with a single, fatal defect. The fortifications ended at the Belgian border. The men who had fashioned them wanted to extend the bunkers, pillboxes, anti-tank traps and blockhouses into Belgium, where the Maginot Line would link up with bastions guarding the Albert Canal and the Meuse River against attack from Germany. Such a Franco-Belgian defensive system might well have discouraged even Hitler. But King

tively large army of twenty divisions (including one armored division) which could be mobilized swiftly in an emergency. The army was highly trained, expertly led, well-armed and finely disciplined. The small Belgian air force had topnotch pilots and modern planes.

Belgium's eastern border, which faced Germany, was heavily fortified, the key to its defenses being Fort Eben Emael, which experts regarded as the world's most powerful single stronghold. A dozen lesser fortresses supported Eben Emael to command the approaches of the Albert Canal and the Meuse River, the portals into Belgium.

By post-World War I standards, Belgium seemed splendidly prepared. But after Hitler's rise to power in Germany, Leopold's advisors urged him to form an alliance with Belgium's old allies, France and England. His Majesty, however, was intransigent and continued to reject that suggestion.

"We shall not again be made the cat's-paw of Perfidious Albion and deceitful France," he declared. Instead, Leopold chose to believe Hitler when the Nazi dictator guaranteed that Germany would "respect for all eternity the borders of Belgium . . ."

His faith in Hitler's word was probably shaken on April 9, 1940, when the Germans invaded neutral Denmark and Norway without provocation or warning. The *Fuehrer* had previously vowed that

Leopold III of Belgium refused to allow any continuation of the Maginot Line across his frontier. With its northern flank thus exposed, the Line could be turned by a determined German push through Belgium.

This unhappy situation resulted from the illogical reasoning of King Leopold, who blamed France, not Germany, for Belgium's ordeal in the First World War. According to Leopold, the Germans had wanted no war in the West in 1914, but the French, by backing Russia against Germany, forced Kaiser Wilhelm to attack France. Since the best route for invading France was through Belgium, the Germans had no choice but to break the neutrality treaty and march into Belgium, Leopold argued.

The fact that his father, King Albert, had defied a German ultimatum seeking permission for the passage of German troops over Belgian soil and instead had chosen to fight, did not sway Leopold's muddied thinking. In his mind, France remained the villain of the 1914–18 drama. This anti-French attitude did not endear Leopold to his people, but the monarch wielded enough influence to block a full military alliance with France and to bar an extension of the Maginot Line onto Belgian territory.

Leopold proclaimed his country's neutrality in any future war and built up the national armed forces. For a small land, Belgium had a compara

Germany wanted nothing from her Scandinavian neighbors. Hitler tried to excuse this aggression by claiming that German intelligence reports indicated the British were about to seize both Denmark and Norway; as a result, he had to forestall the enemy by moving first.

Denmark surrendered in a few hours. Its tiny army could not stand up against the overwhelming forces Hitler threw at the little kingdom. King Christian X, from his palace in Copenhagen, issued a proclamation to his people, urging them to accept the German occupation and maintain "a calm and controlled attitude." The King assured the Danes that he would remain with them. "Your fate is mine," he declared.

Norway gave the Nazis tougher opposition. The Norsemen fought furiously, but *Luftwaffe,* paratroops and native traitors proved too much. The Norwegian campaign lasted only a month, but much German blood was shed before that gallant nation submitted.

King Haakon VII of Norway escaped to London where he set up a government-in-exile. Thousands of his subjects also fled to England, to join the British army or form commando units for hit-and-run attacks along the Norwegian coast.

Though defeated, the Danes and Norse continued to resist the conquerors in a deadly partisan underground struggle which no Nazi terror or treachery could suppress. As the war dragged on, resistance fighters took a heavy toll of the enemy. Eventually, no German dared walk alone after dark in occupied Oslo or Copenhagen.

But the days of the Resistance were still to come. In 1940 Hitler believed the Scandinavian countries had been crushed. With Norway and Denmark in his power, the *Fuehrer* gave the order to launch Code Yellow. The German High Command had overlooked no detail in its preparation. During January, February, March and April, 1940, Nazi agents posing as salesmen, tourists or students entered Holland and Belgium. Scores of them came alone or in small groups, attracting no attention and behaving unobtrusively.

The travelers sipped wine and beer in cafés, strolled city streets and roamed around the countryside. The Dutch and Belgian authorities permitted them to rove without restrictions, unaware that expert eyes were noting every railroad marshaling yard, communication center, highway junction, powerhouse, military installation and airfield. The spies covertly got in touch with local Nazi sympathizers and primed them for action when *Der Tag*—The Day—rolled around.

The Nazis also made masterful use of psychology to intimidate their potential victims. For example, a chain of Amsterdam movie theaters, owned by a German company, ran a documentary film on the conquest of Poland. The *Stuka* dive bombing attacks horrified the viewers as scenes of death, destruction and mutilation flashed across the screen. The Dutch who saw that film came away convinced that anyone who resisted the Germans was doomed.

As he had in all his previous conquests, Hitler found native fifth columnists—traitors who collaborated with the Germans. Norway had its Vidkun Quisling; Holland its Anton Mussert; in Belgium the pro-Fascist society, *Croix-de-feu,* aided the Nazis.

Fifth columnists spread rumors about new German weapons: an undetectable poison gas that blinded and paralyzed; monster tanks that could ford the deepest stream; armor piercing artillery shells; planes capable of incredible speed. As zero hour for Code Yellow drew closer, the whispers became more persistent.

Tensions increased to the point where even a chance remark about the possibility of Nazi attack aroused near panic in Amsterdam. Although neither the Dutch nor the Belgians wished to provoke Hitler, both called reserves to the colors and strengthened frontier posts during the first week of May, 1940, after learning that the Germans had deployed more than 100 divisions (including ten armored) along the borders of Belgium and Holland.

Fifth columnists and Nazi infiltrators intensified their activities. Open sabotage took place in the Lowlands. A Dutch railroad bridge was blown up; fires of mysterious origin broke out in Rotterdam, Antwerp and elsewhere. Factories burned, freight cars were derailed and no night passed without some act of destructive violence. Incident piled on incident. A Brussels radio station was blacked out by a power failure; telephone and telegraph lines were severed; Belgian police shot three men caught trying to dynamite a reservoir wall.

King Leopold's ministers pleaded with him to call upon the French and British for aid before it was too late. British infantry and armored units were poised on the Franco-Belgian border, ready to speed northward at a moment's notice; thousands of French troops awaited orders to cross the frontier. But stubborn Leopold never gave his consent. Despite every evidence that the Germans were massing for a blow, he still clung to the myth of neutrality and warned that he would resist any Allied attempt to place troops on Belgian soil.

Unwilling to provoke such a senseless clash with old comrades-in-arms, the British and French remained in place, morosely watching Hitler prepare to assault the Low Countries.

With the German war machine warming up for the grand thrust, the Dutch moved to protect themselves. Strategic bridges and dikes were readied for demolition. Roadblocks barricaded highways, and heavily reinforced patrols guarded railheads, power stations and similar vital installations.

Calling upon every man to do his duty, Queen Wilhelmina urged her subjects to remain calm. She issued an edict authorizing local military commanders to open dikes and flood wide areas if an enemy crossed Holland's frontiers. Engineer detachments stood by to blow up dams and dikes. The Dutch knew their armed forces could not beat the Germans, but flood waters might slow the enemy until help arrived.

The beautiful May days passed uneasily. Spring's glories were tainted by the preparations for war. Children going off to school noted hooded fear in their mothers' eyes. The morning farewell hug was a lingering one, as though this were a permanent parting and not merely a routine goodbye.

The suspenseful period ended sharply. Late in the evening of May 9, 1940, a Dutch intelligence agent, secretly working across the German border, flashed a five-word radio message: "Tomorrow at dawn! Hold tight!"

That ominous signal alerted the Dutch forces. At sunrise, May 10, Nazi paratroopers came hurtling out of gliders and transport planes. Thousands of German shock units crossed frontier streams, rivers and canals in rubber boats. The waiting Dutch mowed them down by the score, but German reserves kept on coming.

At the same time swarms of *Stukas* plummeted in screaming dives to smash airfields, railroads and communication centers. *Heinkel* bombers and *Messerschmitt* fighters blasted and strafed. Within hours the Dutch air force was annihilated. Tanks lurched across the flat terrain, crashing through the roadblocks. Fifth columnists in Dutch uniforms created confusion behind the lines. Some, disguised as officers, issued false orders to defending forces. Daring Nazi agents seized dikes and bridges before they could be blown up.

By mid-morning the country had become a blazing hell. Civilians, hastily armed at police stations, ran through the streets shooting known Nazi sympathizers on the spot. Boys and girls of high-school and university age took up weapons to fight the Nazis. Farmers and townsmen attacked parachutists with pitchforks and knives; but the Dutch were overwhelmed and the Germans roared ahead everywhere.

About an hour before their attack on Holland, the Germans struck against Belgium. It was still dark when the awesome crash of massed artillery broke the pre-dawn stillness from one end of the Belgian-German frontier to the other.

The Nazis rushed into battle inspired by an Order of the Day from Hitler, who ranted: "My soldiers, the hour has come for the decisive battle for the future of the German nation. . . . The struggle which begins today will decide the fate of the German people for a thousand years! My soldiers, do your duty! *Sieg Heil!*"

Battalions of fanatical SS troops charged Belgian machine-gun positions. They were slaughtered in droves, but no matter how many fell, others rushed to fill the gaps and the Nazis pressed inexorably onward. Hitler used every facet of *blitzkrieg:* planes, tanks, infantry and fifth columnists.

The Germans attacked in two powerful spearheads. One, aimed directly across the border from Aachen, pointed at Fort Eben Emael and its chain of strongpoints. The second raced into southeastern Belgium toward the heavily wooded Ardennes Mountains between the Meuse and Moselle Rivers, a sector only lightly defended because the Belgian General Staff wrongly considered it impassable.

The most thoroughly prepared phase of Code Yellow was the Nazi assault on Fort Eben Emael, where German military efficiency reached its peak. During the winter of 1939–40, hand-picked volunteers had been trained to take the fort. A replica of Eben Emael was built in Germany; Nazi agents in Belgium provided accurate details of the fortress. Engineers and paratroopers rehearsed for weeks until they became familiar with every foot of the fortification.

As German artillery, infantry, aircraft and tanks battered the Belgians, a dozen *Luftwaffe* gliders, handled by specially drilled pilots, descended unseen in the darkness and landed on the flat roof of the giant fortress. Each glider carried twelve men armed with explosives, powerful grenades and demolition equipment. The Nazis dropped their grenades into air vents, rammed explosives down gun muzzles, knocked out observation points and gradually paralyzed the fort.

The garrison, unprepared for such unorthodox tactics, resisted sporadically. It took the Germans only thirty-six hours to capture a stronghold which military observers had considered capable of withstanding any attack. In winning this victory, the Nazis suffered only thirty or forty casualties while the totally demoralized defenders lost some sixty wounded and forty killed.

Even before the sun was high on May 10, 1940, the *Luftwaffe* wiped out more than half the Belgian air force. Every airfield in Belgium was bombed. The *Stukas* also raided dozens of towns and villages, pounding them to blazing rubble.

Soon roads were packed with fleeing people. Vehicles of every type and size crawled along the narrow highways until the routes were choked by humans, machines and animals. Skimming *Messerschmitts* and *Heinkels* strafed the terrified mass with machine guns; wrecked cars, burning trucks, carcasses and bodies blocked the way. The wounded crept into drainage ditches where they died unseen and unheard.

When King Leopold learned the Germans had begun hostilities, he ordered general mobilization and belatedly called upon the French and British for help. The Allies responded promptly. All British forces on the Continent raced pell-mell for Belgium, while portions of three French armies rushed north to meet the Nazis.

One of the greatest battles in history was soon to be joined. Its outcome would affect the lives of millions and reshape the destinies of nations.

# Doomsday

*"...and loud the torrent's roar..."*

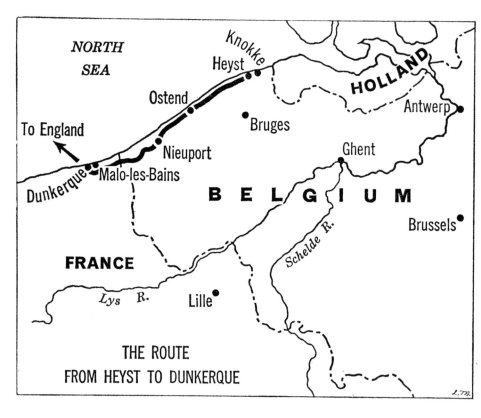

NORTH
SEA

Knokke

Heyst

To England

Ostend

Dunkerque
Malo-les-Bains

Nieuport

Bruges

HOLLAND

Antwerp

Ghent

B E L G I U M

Schelde R.

Brussels

FRANCE

Lys R.

Lille

THE ROUTE
FROM HEYST TO DUNKERQUE

# 1

On that Friday of May, 1940, the sun had hardly risen to the level of the treetops when Justine Raymond waved *au revoir* to her husband Marcel. A portly man in his early forties, he paused on the gravel path that went downhill from the château to the road and returned her gesture before continuing along his way.

As he stepped out on the dirt road to town, a random sun ray which had filtered through the trees glinted off his silver-framed eyeglasses. He walked stolidly, whistling a half-remembered tune. The town, Heyst, on the Belgian seacoast lay at the foot of a gently sloping hill, less than a kilometer from the château.

Marcel was starting the first leg of his daily journey to Brussels, some 70 kilometers away. In Heyst, he would board the 6 A.M. Express for the national capital where he worked as an accountant in the *Banque de Belgique*.

Justine watched until the trees and foliage lining the road hid Marcel from view. The day promised to be perfect. In May, this part of Belgian Flanders, just south of the Dutch border, often enjoyed stretches of flawless weather.

Lingering on the balcony that overlooked the North Sea, Justine smiled at the seagulls soaring and dipping, gliding on the soft breeze, their cries coming to her faintly. The water was smooth and unruffled; lances of sunlight twinkled on the surface as the sun rose higher.

Beyond, to the right, Heyst's whitewashed rooftops sparkled in the sun. The church spire jutted above houses and shops. Smoke puffed from the locomotive of the Brussels Express waiting to begin its run. The scene was peaceful and tranquil; out past the town ran a white-sanded beach which curved snugly around the cove where the fishermen moored their smacks.

The fishing fleet bobbed at anchor. From her vantage point Justine could see dinghies setting off from shore. The fishermen were ready for their morning trip out to sea. Soon all the boats would raise canvas and head for the fishing beds with yellow, blue, red and green sails billowing like gaily colored clouds.

The fishermen of Heyst called the North Sea *notre ami*—our friend. A treacherous friend at times, for those placid waters could turn black and ugly in a storm. Yet even on this day without a trace of foul weather, the sea held hidden perils for the fishing fleet.

Ever since the war started, eight months earlier in September, 1939, the North Sea had become a hazardous passageway for all shipping. Both Germans and British planted thousands of mines in the choppy waters the men of Heyst had to cross each day when they ventured out to the fishing beds. Recently three fishing smacks had been blown up by the mines; and there was mourning in Heyst for the lost men. It mattered little to the victims whether the mines that killed them had been placed there by the British, whom most Belgians looked upon as friends, or by the Germans they still hated because of World War I.

Both Justine and Marcel Raymond had suffered at the hands of the Germans. In 1914 she had lost her father and two brothers, all killed in action. When Marcel was only seventeen, the Germans had put a price on his head for taking part in the underground resistance movement. He managed to escape the Kaiser's secret police and joined the Belgian army in Flanders where he fought until the war ended.

Now war again rocked Europe but unlike 1914 Belgium was not yet a combatant. Her citizens prayed that she would be spared the sufferings of the past. Some hopefully believed it would be possible, but many expected a treacherous German blow. On this day, however, with only the cries of seagulls and the surf splashing on the beach below,

Justine Raymond had no thought of war. She was concerned with more mundane problems.

Smoothing her starched white nurse's uniform, she thought about the committee from the *Confederation des Travailleurs*—the Confederation of Labor—that was coming to see her later that morning. It would be an important visit, headed by Monsieur Charles Mercier, the Confederation's president.

The château in which Justine and Marcel lived was not an ordinary residence. It was called *La Maison des Enfants de Heyst*. A nurse, Justine had been in charge of the institution since 1930 when it was founded by the Confederation as a rest home for children of coal miners, laborers and factory workers who belonged to the Confederation. It was a place where youngsters from poor families, recovering from various illnesses, could be sent at no charge to regain their health and strength.

Fifty patients ranging in age from six to twelve years could be accommodated at *La Maison*. During her time as the home's director, Justine had helped many children. Even the scrawniest responded to the loving care they received at *La Maison*.

Justine Raymond was dedicated to the home and the wan children who passed through it. She worked hard for a small salary because *La Maison* operated on a skimpy budget. She did many jobs: kept accounts, bought food, treated patients, comforted,

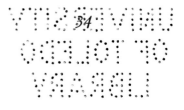

hugged, kissed, scolded and worried about every one of her charges.

In addition to Justine, the staff consisted of three local girls who worked part-time, making beds and taking care of other household chores. The cook, Berthe Ledoux, a sparrow-like woman who had astounding energy and fierce love for the children, had been at *La Maison* since its inception. The only other employee was Marie Bathou, a twenty-year-old nurse, who had herself been a patient at *La Maison* in the first batch that came to the home.

The adult roster was completed by Raoul Jauniaux, the volunteer handyman. Grizzled and white-bearded, he had once been a sailor, but during the First World War he suffered a leg injury when the destroyer on which he served was torpedoed. The old man walked with the aid of a cane, dragging his stiffened right leg for which he received a small pension, his only visible income.

Raoul lived a hermit's existence in a weather-beaten shack on the beach. But every morning, winter or summer, he hobbled up the hill to *La Maison* and did not leave until dark. No one had ever hired him or sent for him; he simply had appeared at the door the day the home officially opened.

"I don't want wages," he said. "I'll work for my food."

Raoul never gave reasons for making the offer and

Justine did not ask. She was grateful for his help. A man of a hundred skills, he knew how to fix leaky faucets or broken tables, and could even repair the home's ten-year-old panel truck.

Although *La Maison* was poor, the ramshackle château rang with laughter. One could hardly believe that the children romping and scampering about the grounds had been listless scarecrows only weeks before.

Justine had worked indefatigably since the arrival of her first patients. A cry in the night still brought her flying to a bedside. She devoted herself to the youngsters of the home. Childless herself, Justine treated each patient as she would her own child; she worked with an intensity that brought her to the brink of physical collapse.

Berthe often scolded Justine for doing too much, but the cook's railings made no impression. Marcel pleaded, argued and stormed. Nothing he said could keep her from performing what she called "duty to the children."

"They've been placed in my hands and I won't fail them," she told her husband. "I must give these babies all my skill, strength and love."

Marcel shrugged his shoulders and flung his arms wide. *"Eh, bien!* The only way to deal with a fanatic is to become one yourself. Now I too am a fanatic," he laughed.

Justine hugged him. "Ah, Marcel, I'm a lucky woman to have you. Such a fine man—"

"Fine man! You mean a wet nurse for fifty youngsters!"

And so ten years drifted by; a parade of passing children, all different, all the same. Each child was etched in Justine's memory. It had been a decade of sorrows, joys, tears and laughter. Years crammed with both happiness and struggle; scrimping to make one *franc* do for five; wrestling with inadequate budgets; fighting to make sick children well and weak ones strong.

Sometimes Justine lost. In an arbor of evergreens near the château stood a row of six small, whitewashed headstones. Spring and summer, gay flowers covered the graves. In the winter they were decked with fir sprigs. Raoul had chiseled the names on the markers and tended the little cemetery among the evergreens where gulls called and rushing surf sounded an eternal lullaby for the children lying beneath the firs.

Justine had dreams for *La Maison*. Instead of the crumbling château, she saw a modern sanatorium with sparkling equipment and a full medical staff. She envisioned a chain of similar rest homes at every spa and seacoast resort in Belgium; places where ailing children could receive free care and proper treatment.

But after ten years *La Maison* still remained the only labor-sponsored children's home in the country. And because so many were waiting for admission, most patients could remain only three months, although many needed longer periods.

Confederation officials were adept at making promises. Year after year the committee pledged improved conditions, and year after year Justine accepted their word. Often a few minor benefits were doled out after a committee visit. Extra supplies might be sent, a small repair made, some gesture to mollify her. She had to be satisfied with these crumbs. There was little choice; either she accepted the committee's dole or she would have to see *La Maison* shut down.

Monsieur Mercier had made these conditions clear to her almost ten years before. A paunchy, bearded man who resembled a genial innkeeper rather than a labor leader and politician, he baldly stated, "I know, *chère amie,* how difficult things are at *La Maison.* But we must be realists. It simply is not possible to raise the funds for everything you ask—"

"Everything, monsieur? Do I want so much? A few sticks of furniture, shoes and new uniforms for the children? Do you expect them to go naked?" Justine had cried.

"Madame, what an idea," Mercier gasped. "Naked, indeed!"

"Well, then? When can I expect a shipment of supplies?"

"Madame, you simply fail to understand. We have no money. If *La Maison* cannot be run on your present budget, we'll have to close our doors."

"Close! Monsieur Mercier, think of the children!"

"That is precisely what I am doing. One day after the Labor Party is in power, we shall be able to give them every luxury. Now we must move slowly and carefully. Our enemies want this experiment to fail. That must never happen," Mercier declared in dramatic tones.

Justine was determined to make *La Maison* succeed and through sheer will power kept the home in operation. But she had grown tired of hand-to-mouth existence. Mercier was now a Labor member in the Chamber of Deputies. He wielded influence and no one in Belgium looked upon *La Maison* as a radical experiment; it had become an accepted institution.

On this Friday in May, Justine had decided to demand everything the home needed. The time was over for worrying about every *franc* she spent. Europe was at war and at any time the holocaust might spread to Belgium. Her children would at least enjoy some of life's luxuries if she had anything to do about it. Smiling a bit, Justine mentally prepared her line of attack on the committee. Charles Mercier would not soon forget May 10, 1940.

She heard Berthe in the kitchen preparing breakfast: porridge, eggs, black bread and hot chocolate.
The stove grate gnashed noisily as the cook shook
down the ashes and stirred the embers. Soon smoke
was trailing from the kitchen chimney. As she always
did while working, Berthe sang tunelessly amid the
rattling of pots and pans.

Raoul limped up the hill, his cane thudding on
the gravel path. He greeted Justine with a nod and
stomped to the toolshed he had built behind the
house. The old man needed no instructions about
his chores. He tackled any job that struck his fancy;
there was always plenty to be done. In a few moments the grinding wheel's whirring and the clash
of metal rising from the shed told Justine he was
sharpening his tools.

Inside the house the grandfather clock on the
staircase chimed six times. In the distance the town's
church tower clock tolled the hour. The last note
was still vibrating when the locomotive whistle
screeched a final warning and the 6 A.M. train left
Heyst for Brussels.

Their sails swelling in a freshening breeze, the
fishing smacks skimmed out of the cove to the open
sea. The town stirred awake. Milkmen's carts rattled over the cobbled streets. Shutters banged open.
Church bells summoned worshippers to early mass.
Men pedaled to work on bicycles, lunch pails dangling from the handlebars.

Bony horses pulled carts loaded with produce from surrounding farms to the market where early comers were setting up displays of eggs, cabbages, cheeses, smoked meats and butter. Fishmonger stalls were heaped with herrings, flounder, sole, a dozen varieties taken from the North Sea. Chickens hung beside redolent sausages and slabs of beef in the butcher shops.

Heyst shook off sleep. Children scurried to bake-shops for *brioches* and *croissants,* the Belgian's traditional breakfast rolls. Nothing seemed amiss that Friday morning. At 6 A.M. no one in Heyst suspected that Doomsday had dawned. A world was about to crumble and the survivors of the holocaust were destined to endure some of the most brutal terror ever inflicted on mankind.

# 2

It has often happened that a catastrophe such as an earthquake has destroyed a city, while only a few miles away everything continued normally, with no sign of the disaster. So it was on the morning the Germans invaded Belgium. The frontier regions flamed in furious battle; men died, villages burned. But less than 100 kilometers away, on the seacoast, gulls screeched and wheeled in the sunshine. Waves lapped the beaches and fishing boats dotted the horizon.

The news of the German attack did not reach Heyst until 6:30 A.M. when the Brussels radio announced that war had begun and general mobilization was ordered. A housewife, who heard the broadcast, poked her head out the window and screamed, "War! We are at war with the *boches!*"

Passersby looked up at her, shook their heads and walked on.

"Madame, you're drunk!" a man laughed.

"She's not drunk, she's crazy," another jeered, tapping his forehead with a finger.

Within seconds they knew she was neither. People

dashed from their houses shouting and gesticulating. Men cursed, women wept and frightened children bawled. "War! War!" they yelled over and over again.

A near riot broke out in the market place when a fear-stricken mob stampeded through the square, upsetting stalls, crushing eggs and trampling vegetables underfoot. The market became a welter of mauling, shrieking people. Above the babel rose the cry: "The *boches!* The Germans! The Germans!"

Tumult became panic when a single airplane flew over the town. "That's a *Stuka!*" someone shouted.

Screaming in terror, the throng charged first one way, then the other. A woman, clutching her whimpering child, crouched beneath a wooden cart that offered no protection at all. Some of the crowd flung themselves on the cobblestones and lay prone. Men clawed to get through the narrow doorways of nearby stores and cafes. A little girl sat in the open, crying.

After the panic spent itself, the confusion subsided. No bombs came hurtling down; no *Stukas* dropped death from the sky. As they realized that it had been a false alarm, people rose from the pavement and emerged shame-faced from hiding places, cringing at their cowardly behavior. Fear had drained them of pride, dignity and courage.

The unnatural silence that blanketed Heyst was

unexpectedly broken by clanging church bells sounding an insistent summons. The mob drifted to the *Place de l'Eglise* and gathered in front of the church. Soon the market place was empty, except for a few old men and women picking through ruined vegetables and smashed egg crates.

A truckload of soldiers from Bruges, the nearest large city, rolled into the *Place de l'Eglise*. The troops, in combat dress and carrying rifles, leaped from the truck. A second army vehicle which had loudspeakers mounted on its roof cruised into the *Place*.

"Citizens of Heyst," the loudspeakers blared metallically, "the Germans have crossed our borders. We are at war. Reservists report to your units at once. This area has been declared a military zone. It is believed enemy agents may be operating in this region. Be on the alert. Advise the authorities of any strangers acting suspiciously. Let every Belgian do his duty with honor. Long live the King! Long live Belgium!"

The sound truck bounced away, martial music rattling from its horns. With rifles slung, the soldiers marched through town toward the beach. The crowd dispersed reluctantly; the people did not seem to understand how this calamity had befallen them and their frenzy gave way to disbelief.

The church tower chimed seven times. When it last had tolled the hour, war had been a vague menace. In other parts of Europe the conflict was a deadly epidemic which did not affect Belgium. Now the plague had crossed boundary lines and the land would soon be torn and ravaged. This bright morning in May, death and devastation were unwelcome visitors in Belgium.

# 3

Daily at 6:30 A.M. Justine rang the big, brass hand bell she called "The Awakener." It sounded a clangorous reveille that morning, as usual. The children arose grudgingly, but once fully awake, young voices shrilled through the house in a volcano of talk, laughter and chatter. At 6:45 A.M., the bell called them to breakfast.

Down the stairs they bounded in faded, pale blue denim uniforms, ready to begin the day's activities, even those with cheeks still sunken and eyes too bright from the fever that had racked their frail bodies.

They jostled into the once elegant dining *salon*. Each waited by his place at one of the long tables set with mugs, bowls and silverware. Justine presided over the table for the older children while Marie supervised the feeding of the younger ones.

As was her custom, Justine called cheerily, *"Bonjour, mes enfants!"*

The responses came in a high-pitched chorus: *"Bonjour, Tante Justine!"*

The greeting was followed by scraping benches

*46*

and clattering silverware as the children sat down. Berthe wheeled in a serving cart carrying a huge tureen filled with steaming porridge which she ladled out into the bowls as she passed. Three older boys, acting as waiters, helped her by bringing earthenware pitchers brimful of hot chocolate and platters of eggs and black bread to the tables.

The children ate quickly. This was a school day. All those able to do so walked the kilometer into town. The rest were transported by bus. Though the boys and girls were with her only a short time, Justine tried to keep their lives normal, which included attendance at school.

At seven o'clock, as the meal was ending, Raoul appeared at the dining room door. He beckoned to Justine, waving his stick to attract her attention. Puzzled by his action, she went to him.

The old man pointed with the cane. Standing in the château's entrance were an army lieutenant and two soldiers. "Why are they here?" Justine asked.

Raoul's eyes brimmed. "The Germans," he mumbled. Tears spilled down his leathery cheeks.

Justine hurried to the men in the doorway. The lieutenant and the soldiers were very young. To Justine they seemed like boys. The steel helmets were too big, the packs too heavy, the rifles too long. Shuffling uncomfortably under her scrutiny the lieutenant cleared his throat. "Madame, I have bad news. The Germans attacked us this morning."

"You mean—war!" Justine gasped.

"Yes, madame. Nazi planes have already bombed all our airfields. They hit Knokke about an hour ago," the officer said, mentioning a field only a few kilometers north of Heyst, on the coast near the Dutch border.

Justine gestured toward the noisy dining room. "My children—they'll be leaving for school—"

"Not today, madame. School's out. The army's taking over Heyst."

"Do you think it's safe here for the children?"

"I don't know. Who's safe? The *boches* invaded Holland too. It's Poland, Norway and Denmark all over again. Planes, tanks, everything. My captain said they've also come through Luxembourg. So I don't know who's safe, madame."

"I can't let anything happen to my children," Justine said.

"It's out of your hands, madame. What will be, will be. If I can help in any way, please call on me. Lieutenant Paul Duval, second platoon, Fifth Company, Thirty-ninth Infantry. We're down below on the beach."

"Yes, yes, thank you, Lieutenant."

"I know how difficult it must be with all these youngsters to look after—" Duval hesitated, flapped his hands awkwardly and turned to his soldiers. "Move out, men," he said gruffly. The three of them left.

*48*

Raoul jabbed his stick in their direction. "Boys fighting wars. Boys! Ah, those damned *boches*. Didn't they do enough to us the last time?"

Justine stared at him numbly and then clapped a hand over her mouth. "Oh, dear God! They'll be calling up the reservists! Marcel—"

"I'm sorry, madame. It's only the old wrecks like me they can't use," Raoul said bitterly.

"I'll call him at the bank. He must be in Brussels by now," Justine mused aloud. "Raoul, please tell Marie to keep the children in the dining room. I'll be there soon."

The old man nodded. "I'll see they stay put."

Justine went down the hall to the small room she used as an office. It had a battered desk, a rickety chair, an old typewriter and a scarred filing cabinet. Peeling paint flaked from the wall. There was a calendar over the desk and a framed group photograph of *La Maison's* first patients. Papers, notes, bills and letters were skewered on a spindle spike that stood beside the telephone on the desk.

Justine picked up the receiver and waited for the operator. After a long delay, a tearful voice responded, "Heyst Central."

"Brussels, please," Justine said, giving the number.

"I can't get through. The lines are dead," the operator sobbed. "It's the Germans!"

Justine sat mutely for a few moments, then hung

up the receiver and walked to the dining room with slow, heavy steps.

She paused on the threshold, gazing numbly at the children. They turned to her, laughing, eager, waiting for her to speak. She compressed her lips tightly and held up a hand for silence.

"*Mes enfants*, I have something important to tell you," she said, surprised at the calmness of her voice. "Something very important."

# Exodus

"...amid confused alarms
of struggle and flight..."

At about 9 A.M. Heyst had its first taste of war when three *Stuka* dive bombers, with sunlight dancing on their silvery bodies, came to blast the beach where Duval's platoon was digging in. As the bombs whistled down, the soldiers scurried for cover, running awkwardly in the sand.

Duval shouted orders that went unheard. The *Stukas* climbed steeply and dived again, raking the beach with machine guns. Bullets kicked up spurts of sand but caused no casualties. After the second pass the planes winged off, heading out to sea.

As the bombs crashed and the machine guns chattered, the children of *La Maison* came bursting out of the house. They ran about excitedly, watching the planes and crying out to each other.

"Look there! Look!" a tow-haired twelve-year-old exclaimed, pointing to a diving *Stuka*.

"It's like a silver bird!" a six-year-old said.

Justine and Marie shooed the youngsters back into the château. Raoul limped in, his beard bristling, his cheeks aflame with fury.

"You little idiots," he shouted at the children,

shaking his stick. "Those are *boches* up there! I ought to spank every one of you! Don't you have any sense? Are you trying to get yourselves killed?"

Startled by his outburst, several children began to cry. Raoul's tirade brought Berthe from the kitchen. She shook a long, bony forefinger at him.

"Stop bullying these poor darlings," she snapped. "Can't you see how you've frightened them?"

"I'm trying to put some sense in their heads. Airplanes kill children too!"

"Well, that's no way to treat my babies," Berthe said. "Frightening them half to death—"

"No, no, Mademoiselle Berthe," a skinny, blonde boy of twelve interrupted. "Monsieur Raoul is right. We were stupid to go out when the *boches* were bombing."

"Thanks, Georges," Raoul grunted. "At least somebody here can use his brains. You're a smart boy. I know you won't run around like a fool when the *boches* come again."

"Do you think they'll be back?" Justine asked anxiously.

Raoul shrugged. "One never knows, but I think they will pay us another visit."

Justine shook her head. "What shall we do, Raoul? Suppose they bomb us? The château—"

"What can be done, madame? One prays they'll miss and that the bombs will hit somewhere else."

"You're the only one who knows about war,

54

Raoul. Show us what to do if there's another air raid," Justine said.

Raoul tugged at his beard. "The cellar is safest during a bombing. We'll fix it as a shelter. Then we'll need some kind of warning system. I'll rig up an alarm."

He fashioned a crude air-raid alarm from an iron bar which was suspended on a low tree branch a few feet from the front door. When rapped with a hammer, the bar gave out a loud, clanging noise.

Raoul demonstrated this for the assembled children. They paid strict attention, watching his every move. "Now when you hear that sound, head straight for the cellar, no matter what else you're doing." Raoul drew his bushy brows together and scowled fiercely. "That means everybody! Unless you want to be blown to bits!"

He picked up the hammer. "Let's see if you understood what I told you." Suddenly he hit the bar a hard whack. It rang discordantly. No one moved until Raoul hit it again. Only then the boy Georges jumped up and cried, "To the cellar, everybody. Quickly!"

The children made a rush for the door, pushing and scrambling to get inside. They tumbled into the hallway, laughing and shoving. The adults reacted slowly. The third time Raoul struck the bar, Justine, Marie and Berthe hurried to the house, gathering up stray children as they ran.

At last they were all down in the cellar, the young-sters shrieking in delight at this strange game. Raoul appeared at the head of the stairs.

"Quiet down there!" he bellowed furiously. "Are you a flock of sheep? Do you think this is play?"

He ordered them out and made them repeat the drill a dozen times, until it was carried out with swift discipline. Finally, when everyone was red-faced, panting and sweaty, Raoul seemed satisfied.

"All right," he said. "I think you have the idea. Now there's still lots of work to do. The next time you hear the alarm, it won't be a drill. Your life depends on getting to the cellar without delay."

He stared hard for a moment at the young faces grouped around him. After a few seconds Raoul pointed to Georges and three other twelve-year-old boys. "Georges, Claude, Jacques and Louis. I have a special job for the four of you. You're going to be our air-raid wardens. Do you know what that means?"

"*Oui,* monsieur," Jacques said. He was a plump boy, whose eyeglasses gave him the appearance of a troubled schoolmaster. "We must watch for *boche* planes and give the warning when they come."

"That's it," Raoul grinned, ruffling the boy's hair. "It's a big responsibility. Keep your eyes peeled. If you spot a *boche,* hit the bar as hard as you can and then head for the cellar yourselves. You're in charge of the wardens, Georges. See that everyone stays on the job."

Young Georges nodded gravely. "We will do our best, monsieur." He walked out unsmiling, followed by the others. Four little boys suddenly thrust into manhood. Only that morning they had been children. As they left to take their posts, Justine remembered with a pang that Jacques sometimes had bad dreams and cried in his sleep.

She stood beside Raoul in the doorway and watched the boys. They consulted for a moment and then trotted off to four different points from which there was an unobstructed view of the sky. Each peered upward, eyes shielded against the sun, scanning the blue above them.

"What a pity," Justine said. "My youngsters doing this."

"Madame, war is ugly and is made even uglier because no one can be protected from it. No one. Not even innocent children." He sighed heavily. "We mustn't waste any time, madame. There's a lot to be done."

Under his direction the château was readied for an air raid. Raoul nailed boards across the windows. He ordered buckets of water carried to the cellar; blankets and mattresses were brought there; tins of food and other staples were also stored below.

Everyone, even the smallest child, worked hard.

By noon the task had been completed. Everyone was sitting down to lunch when the air-raid alarm clanged.

"To the cellar!" Justine cried.

Precisely as they had been trained to do, the children filed down without confusion, guided by Justine, Marie and Berthe, who had hurried from the kitchen still clutching the ladle with which she had been dishing out soup.

The front door flew open and Georges rushed in followed by his fellow wardens. *"Boche* planes! Lots of them!" he gasped. "Heading for Heyst!"

Raoul, who had been outside, stomped in behind them. "They must be after the railroad. Come on, don't stand talking. The cellar!"

They waited in the gloom of the damp stone basement, every face upturned, listening. Airplane motors droned louder and louder until they drummed a cataract of noise. An explosion jarred, then another and another. Upstairs the impact sent some heavy object crashing to the floor. The children huddled together, clutching each other. Justine locked her arms around a sobbing girl and held her tightly.

The bombs fell so rapidly that their explosions overlapped. Mortar dust drifted into the cellar as the detonations rocked the château. Children began to cry. One boy fell to the floor shrieking. Raoul lifted him up and growled, "Stop that or I'll shake your teeth loose!" The outburst ended in a muffled gasp.

Raoul drew his bushy brows together in a furious scowl. "I'm ashamed of all of you. I thought you were brave. Let's show the *boches* we're not afraid. Sing, everybody! Come on, sing!"

The next moment his deep baritone topped the noise of the bombs, as he sang: *"Sur le pont, d'Avignon, on y danse, on y danse. . . ."*

He sang alone for a few seconds until Justine took up the tune. Then, one by one, the rest chimed in as Raoul kept time, using his cane for a baton.

"You can do better," he cried. "Louder! Sing louder!"

So they sang over and over about the bridge at Avignon, the gay, lilting child's song, accompanied by a chorus of crashing bombs.

# 2

When the raid ended, silence came as a surprise. As the bombs stopped falling the singing died away. No one spoke or moved in the stillness until Justine asked, "Is it over?"

"I think so," Raoul nodded. He pulled a watch from his jacket pocket and squinted at the dial. "Ten minutes—only ten minutes—"

"It was a lifetime," Justine whispered. She clapped her hands for attention. "We're going upstairs now, *mes enfants.*"

"Not yet. Let me take a look around first," Raoul cautioned.

"Be careful," Justine warned.

Raoul chuckled. "Don't worry, madame, I'm not tired of living yet."

In a moment, he called from the head of the cellar stairs. "All clear. They're gone, for sure."

Justine emerged from the cellar with the children and gaped in dismay. The hallway was littered with rubble. The grandfather clock had toppled face down on the staircase landing. The air hung thick with plaster dust. Cracks gaped in a wall of the dining *salon* and a blast had blown dishes off the tables so the floor was strewn with broken crockery. Berthe dashed through the damaged room to the kitchen, the others crowding behind. Cutlery, pots, pans and cooking utensils were scattered helter-skelter. A huge iron kettle had fallen from the stove and soup was pouring out of it to form a steaming puddle on the stone kitchen floor.

"Oh! Oh! My soup! Those Nazi swine!" Berthe screeched.

Miraculously the damage to *La Maison* was not major; although the château had been shaken by bombs, it had not received a direct hit. The town of Heyst was less fortunate. Columns of smoke, rising in greasy black spirals, almost obscured it. Flames licked at the church spire and danced across the rooftops.

Justine and the children looked upon the awful scene from the hilltop. The trees on the road leading to Heyst had been mutilated. Some lay ripped out of the earth with roots exposed like torn arteries.

Watching the fires in Heyst through tear-misted eyes, Justine felt she was a spectator watching the end of the world. In that terrible moment her thoughts turned to Marcel. Where was he? What had happened to him? Was this how they were destined to end their life together, miles apart, neither able to comfort the other?

A fusillade of shots brought her abruptly back to reality. "Children, get inside!" she cried.

Before anyone could move, two men in civilian clothes were seen running on the road below. Several yards behind came Lieutenant Duval, revolver in hand. A knot of soldiers followed him. Rifles cracked and the fleeing men pitched forward, skidding face down in the road. Duval approached them cautiously, then called to his soldiers who gathered around the two bodies.

The lieutenant looked up and saw the group watching from the hill. Speaking to the soldiers again, he holstered the revolver and strode up the path to where Justine was standing.

"Sorry you had to see this," he said.

"Why did you shoot them? Who were they?" Justine asked.

"Fifth columnists, signaling Nazi planes from the beach. They ran for it instead of giving up." Duval clenched his fists helplessly. "This stupid war!"

"There's lots worse to come, Lieutenant. Take a look at Heyst. Don't worry about traitors. Save your sympathy for decent people," Raoul advised.

"I've never killed anyone before. I'm not used to war, old-timer," Duval said.

"And you never will be, Lieutenant," Raoul said.

"I guess not. How did you come through the raid? Anybody hurt?"

"We were lucky. Lieutenant, listen, can you find

us a couple of vehicles to move these children away?"

"I don't know. I'll be in touch with my regimental commander at Bruges—"

"Wait!" Justine cut in. "I won't pack the children off God knows where. They're staying here until I get word from the Confederation. Besides their parents must be informed. I'll wait until instructions come—"

"Which may be never!" Raoul interrupted. "You can't even put a phone call through to Brussels. You must go away while there's still time!"

"Not without orders," Justine insisted. "That will be all, Raoul!"

"Yes, madame," the old man growled.

"I'll send the message anyway," Duval promised. "Perhaps headquarters can reach the Confederation people. Meanwhile, keep under cover, madame. The *Stukas* may return."

"Yes, Lieutenant," Justine said.

Duval went to his men. Some soldiers arrived with stretchers and the group straggled off, taking the bodies with them.

German planes were overhead all afternoon and did not leave until nightfall. At dusk a flight of *Stukas* wiped out Duval's beach position. Other dive bombers caught the Heyst fishing fleet. Within minutes every boat was either burning or sinking.

The children remained in the basement until

after dark. They came out only when the planes finally flew off. Berthe prepared a makeshift meal for them, but most of the youngsters fell asleep while eating. The older boys and Raoul helped them back to the cellar where beds had been improvised.

Justine went outside. The fires burning in Heyst cast a red glow against the sky. Out on the water fiery splotches marked the blazing fishing fleet. Alone in the darkness, Justine wept silently; but after a minute or two, she regained control. This was no time for either tears or despair. Drawing herself erect, she strode stiffly back to the old house, silhouetted against the scarlet background of burning Heyst.

The first day of war had ended.

# 3

*La Maison* stood on its scarred hillside cut off from the outside world, with the telephone dead and every radio station in the country silenced by Nazi bombs. All electric power was out. Water had to be hand-hauled from the well. Lacking instructions from the Confederation, Justine was isolated with her children amid the smoldering ruin wrought by the *Stukas*.

At daybreak, Saturday, May 11, Raoul went to the beach. He returned gray-faced and shaken. The planes had killed Lieutenant Duval and all his men.

"As usual, the *boches* were thorough," he said.

Later, he ventured into Heyst, driving the rattletrap truck over the bomb-pitted roads and was gone so long that Justine feared something had happened to him. But in the afternoon the ancient truck came chugging up the hill. Raoul brought news and it was all bad.

Heyst had been leveled, the town reduced to rubble with nearly every house either damaged or destroyed. Numbed, dazed people stumbled about "like sleepwalkers," according to Raoul. Dead and wounded were buried beneath the wreckage. The army had sent doctors, medical supplies and rations from Bruges, but *Stukas* blasted the convoys and only a few vehicles got through.

According to reports and rumors Raoul had gathered, the Belgian army was still fighting though Fort Eben Emael had fallen. The hard-pressed Belgians were falling back from main defenses along the Albert Canal, seeking to form a new line from Antwerp to Louvain. Freshly arrived British and French units were digging in on a front that extended between Louvain and Wavre.

Despite the "Tommies" and *poilus* (slang for British and French soldiers), Nazi *panzers* were rampaging about the countryside at will, finding weak spots for the fast-moving, motorized German infantry.

Civilian refugees were forced to help the invaders. Nazi shock units used them as human shields, driving the people before them. When a strong point was reached, the Belgian defenders hesitated to fire on their own countrymen, which allowed the Germans to come within striking distance. When they were close enough, the Nazis shot the hostages and overwhelmed the bastion. This cruel tactic had been repeated at many points. Masses of civilians were also sent across minefields to clear the way for Hitler's soldiers.

With Belgian air strength annihilated, the *Luft-*

*waffe* roved the skies meeting only limited opposition from Royal Air Force *Spitfires* and French fighters. The military situation was grim. The Nazis had the advantage of surprise against a weaker, unprepared foe. King Leopold's policy of clinging to the false security of a neutrality backed by Hitler's pledge was shown as a tragic mistake. His stand had brought on the very calamity he had hoped to prevent.

The news spread gloom over *La Maison*. Even the six-year-olds understood that disaster had overtaken them. No laughter sounded in the hallway or on the grounds. The children went about like shadows—silent, withdrawn, obedient.

"They're like scared puppies," Berthe grumbled. "It breaks my heart to see them this way. And here I can't even put out a decent meal." Food was her cure-all. When trouble pressed, or a crisis arose, Berthe was always ready with "a nice cup of tea," "a bowl of soup" or "a sandwich," as though the processes of digestion could solve every problem.

This was one time that a royal banquet would not have helped and even Berthe knew it. At any moment German planes might finish everything with a shower of bombs. However, no enemy aircraft came that day or on Sunday. If not for the smoke still billowing from the ruins of Heyst, the pitted earth, the mutilated trees and blackened foliage, the war might have been only the product of a twisted imagination. It seemed to have passed on like a tropical storm which brought death and havoc but was soon followed by sunny, placid skies.

Despite the lull, precautions at *La Maison* were not relaxed. Georges and his faithful airplane spotters stayed on duty. The pause in the bombing enabled Justine, Raoul, Berthe and Marie, assisted by the children, to tidy up the cellar.

Cooking was solved when Raoul fixed an old kerosene stove and set it up in the basement. He foraged fuel for it somehow. Berthe soon had a mouthwatering soup bubbling away. Everyone ate the meager meal with gusto. Bowls were emptied and chunks of black bread devoured.

"Wasn't any feast but it's better than going hungry," Berthe smiled, as she watched the children.

Sunday afternoon, spirits were lifted when a convoy of lorries carrying Belgian infantrymen rolled past *La Maison* on their way to the Dutch border. The soldiers looked fit and cheerful. The children ranged along the roadside waving them on.

The battered survivors of Heyst saw hope in the youthful soldiers riding so bravely northward. Perhaps they could stop the Germans. Those who remembered the First War spoke of "stabilizing the front." Then, aided by the Tommies and *poilus,* they would eventually triumph as in 1914–18.

This time too the sturdy Dutch, neutral in the last conflict, were on their side. The Germans had to face a resolute enemy in Holland and the Dutch had a powerful ally—the sea. Once the dikes were opened, torrents of water would sweep across the flat land to form an impassable barrier; the *panzers* would be mired in bogs and German soldiers drowned by the thousands.

They clung to this fantasy, blocking out the truth; Holland's army was small with less than a dozen squadrons of planes and few modern anti-aircraft guns. The Hollanders made good soldiers, but the nation had been at peace for more than a century. The present-day Dutch army had never fired a shot in anger; its generals, officers, non-coms and soldiers were only students of warfare, not practitioners of it.

Nazi paratroopers and fifth columnists moved so swiftly on May 10 that demolition parties, posted to blow bridges and dikes, were wiped out before the charges could be set. In those places where sluice gates had been opened, the land did not flood fast enough and German tanks raced on unimpeded. The sea that finally submerged Holland's farmlands annoyed the Germans without either hindering or stalling them.

"We had pitted our ancient weapon against the modern juggernaut, trusting that the forces of nature could overwhelm the enemy as the Red Sea drowned the Egyptians who were pursuing the Israelites. Unfortunately, the Old Testament strategy did not work for us. In this case the forces of evil destroyed the good," a Dutch army officer said.

By Monday, May 13, the end was near for Holland. The army had been decimated; units were isolated and only pockets of resistance still continued to fight. The *panzers* crisscrossed all Holland, while the *Luftwaffe* kept up an unending bombardment; fires burned out of control so that whole areas writhed in flames. From the air, according to a Nazi pilot, "the land resembled a gigantic bed of glowing coals. . . ."

The Dutch declared Rotterdam an open city to spare that ancient seaport from air attacks or artillery bombardment. But the Germans paid no heed and pounded it with heavy caliber guns. This left the Dutch commander no alternative but to resist.

On May 14 the Dutch were given a three-hour ultimatum to surrender or else suffer "the total destruction of Rotterdam by aerial bombing. . . ." A few minutes after the deadline, the Dutch forces capitulated, but the Germans, worried that Rotterdam might be used as a base for British troops to land in Holland, decided to finish off the city. Even after the Dutch surrender message had been received, Nazi *Heinkels* and *Stukas* were sent off on a murderous mission.

"Wipe out Rotterdam!" the pilots were ordered. With no opposition except from desultory anti-aircraft fire, the Nazi aerial armada unleashed a tremendous bombardment on the city.

In only seven and one-half minutes, the heart of Rotterdam was destroyed; two square miles were laid waste and nearly 50,000 helpless civilians killed. The liner *Statendam,* the 28,000-ton queen of the Dutch merchant fleet, lay wrecked and burning in the harbor. It was a cruel and barbarous attack, a needless slaughter—Dutch resistance already had been broken.

The following day, May 15, General Henri Winkelman, commander-in-chief of the Dutch army, formally surrendered to prevent further bloodshed. In five days his army had suffered over 100,000 casualties.

The German victory was not quite complete. The Nazis lost one prize when Queen Wilhelmina of Holland escaped to England on a British destroyer. Royal Navy vessels successfully evacuated a battalion of Irish and Welsh Guards and some 200 Royal Marines from the Hook of Holland where they had been sent to assure the Queen's escape.

While these crucial events were taking place in Holland, the Nazis kept advancing through Belgium. Lieutenant General Ewald von Kleist broke through the supposedly impassable Ardennes Forest with *panzers* and shock troops. He crossed the Meuse River and opened a 50-mile-wide gap through which the *panzers* poured in a headlong dash for the English Channel at Abbeville.

While the Germans were slashing the Belgian, British and French armies in Belgium and destroying the Dutch, the war, which had given *La Maison* a forty-eight-hour breathing spell, returned in another form.

On Monday, May 13, the van of a pitiable procession stumbled southward on the coastal road. It was a motley parade of civilian refugees fleeing the carnage in Holland, an avalanche of miserable humanity that kept swelling as more and still more people joined the throng seeking sanctuary.

The pushing, jostling crowd straggled in disarray. Some pulled carts piled high with bedding or furniture. Horse-drawn wagons, bicycles, cars and trucks were trapped in a monstrous traffic snarl.

This was the backwash of the Nazi invasion. Europe had never known such an exodus. The Germans were deliberately driving the multitudes onto the roads. The *Stukas* concentrated on bombing railroads so thoroughly that not a single train could move anywhere in Belgium or Holland. The only escape route was by road and as the Germans had planned, the human flood hindered reinforcements trying to reach the front.

Allied soldiers on foot, in trucks and tanks, were engulfed by the human tide swarming from the opposite direction. At one point, British tankmen fired machine guns in the air to scatter the refugees. But the people plodded on, staring dully at the tankers. They were terrified beyond fear and agonized past pain.

Only days earlier they had been farmers, workers, clerks, housewives and students. Now their sane world was smashed. All that once had been important no longer counted. Social standing and prestige were wiped out. Rich and poor, ignorant and learned, young and old, marched in that faceless, formless mass.

Under the bombs no man was better than another; his only asset was life itself. Bombs and machine-gun bullets heeded neither rank nor wealth; landlord and tenant shared the same death. The *Stukas* had leveled more than buildings. Their bombs broke long-standing barriers of class and caste. A democracy almost impossible to attain during peacetime was born in the suffering and anguish of war.

# 4

Refugees overran *La Maison*. People slept on the floor, the stairs, wherever they found room. Scores collapsed on the grounds. The hillside was dotted with huddled figures lying where they had fallen.

Exhausted wanderers cried for water, their voices rising in a hideous wail. One saw unbearable sights: a young mother still clutched her dead baby; an old man coughed out his life; three Dutch children, who had lost their parents somewhere on the terrible march, sat howling like stricken animals.

The crowd on the road grew thicker. The day was warm and the thousands of unwashed bodies gave off an odor that fouled the air for miles. Choking dust hung over the slow-moving throng in clouds that almost blotted out the sun.

The southbound trek went on all day Monday, May 13, and continued until Wednesday, May 15. The thirsty, hungry horde came like a swarm of locusts. Desperate foragers raided farms along the way, stealing eggs, chickens, fruit, anything that could be carried off. They scrabbled in vegetable patches to dig up carrots, radishes, turnips and left the fields bare. Peasants attacked the invaders with clubs, pitchforks, rakes and scythes. Fierce brawls broke out as the marauders fought with each other and the farmers.

So many people drank at one stream that it was drained dry. Wells and cisterns in the path of that voracious horde were emptied to the last drop. Pillagers broke into *La Maison's* larder, carrying off all the food as the inhabitants looked on helplessly. Blankets, mattresses and cooking utensils were stolen and someone even drove off in the old truck.

The crowd slowly lessened. Those who had crammed into *La Maison* gradually trickled away. By the afternoon of May 15, the road was deserted except for some stragglers. Only the dead and dying still sprawled on the hillside. The human flow stopped only because the Germans had trapped many thousands at the Dutch border and herded them south along other roads to impede advancing British and French troops.

As quiet replaced the uproar and the last refugee wandered off, Justine slumped on a lower step of the staircase. The children gathered around, looking at her with questioning eyes, searching for reassurance.

The adults also turned to Justine. Raoul leaned on his cane. Berthe dabbed at her eyes with the corner of her apron. Marie, her face streaked and smudged, leaned against a wall. All kept their eyes fixed on Justine.

For the first time she was ready to admit defeat. Even at the worst of the bombing and the height of the refugee invasion, Justine had not known the fear that now overpowered her. *La Maison* had once been a symbol of security; this aged château, which had withstood the brunt of storms and wars in the past, no longer offered protection. How could they stay there without food and no place to get any? Perhaps the only choice was to await the Germans. The refugees had told her the *boches* were advancing south at great speed. They would be coming soon.

Justine did not care what they did to her if she could be certain the youngsters would not be harmed. But she remembered accounts of Nazi cruelty in Poland where the Germans had spared neither young nor old; and stories of German brutality in Belgium during the 1914–18 war. Why should the *boches* act differently this time?

She thought again of Marcel. There had been no word from him since Friday. She recalled his departure that morning and saw him again, going down the path to the road, sunlight winking off his glasses.

She wondered where he was—dead or wounded perhaps; caught by strafing planes or crushed beneath a tank. Death had many faces in war. Dear Marcel. A gentle, uncomplaining man. Because she wanted to be director of *La Maison,* he willingly made the tiresome journey to and from Brussels every weekday morning and evening; he understood her need to work with children. Their own infant son died in 1926 and they had learned she could not have another child. How long ago that seemed—1926—the boy would have been fourteen, a young man.

They had endured sorrow, she and Marcel; but even in the darkest time, he had remained cheerful and optimistic. Marcel was gone. Possibly she would never see him again. She found this hard to accept. They had parted that fatal Friday as they did every day; she had been given no chance to thank him for all their years together.

Marcel was neither distinguished nor brilliant. He had not won fame or wealth. Although he was an ordinary man of ordinary attainments, he had fine qualities: integrity, honesty, courage, tenderness and understanding.

Justine's thoughts were interrupted by Raoul. "Madame, it won't do any good brooding about what's happened. We've got to find some food. These young ones must eat," he said.

"That's right," Berthe wailed, breaking into tears. "They left us nothing! Not a morsel, not a crumb! What will become of us?"

"Stop that crying!" Raoul ordered. "I can't think with you wailing in my ears!"

Berthe stopped crying and turned on Raoul. Lips compressed, arms akimbo, she glared at him indignantly.

"Don't use that tone to me," she snapped, moving slowly toward Raoul.

The old man raised a hand. "Just a minute, Berthe. I didn't mean—"

Shaking a finger under his nose, the angry cook rasped, "Another word and I'll pull out your beard, a hair at a time!"

Raoul pulled back as though drawing away from a sudden fire. "Berthe, I wasn't—I—" He turned pleadingly to Justine. "Madame, please—"

The sight of the fierce old sailor retreating from the skinny cook made the children laugh. Justine also began to laugh and merry peals filled the hallway, until even Raoul and Berthe joined the mirth.

At last Raoul stopped, gasping for breath. Pulling out a crumpled bandanna, he wiped his streaming eyes. "Ah, that's what we all needed, a good laugh." He grinned at Berthe and thrust out his hand. "Sorry I spoke so sharply to you. Friends?"

She shook his hand. "Friends." She smiled.

"Now let's be practical," Raoul said. "The youngsters need food and so do we. That's the main thing."

"Aha! Listen to him. Food! But where will we get it?" Berthe asked.

"I don't know," Raoul said. "There's nothing left?"

"I told you—nothing. Even my pots and pans are gone."

Justine rose slowly to her feet. "I have something to say. Marie, please take the children to the cellar. I want a word with Raoul and Berthe."

"Yes, madame," Marie nodded. She beckoned and the children followed her down the hall. When they were out of earshot, Justine spoke quietly. "I want you both to leave. Take Marie along, you may be able to reach France where you'll be safe."

"Do you expect us to abandon you and the children?" Raoul demanded.

"Yes."

"Madame Raymond!" Berthe cried. "I'd never even consider it! Never!"

"If I wait here the Germans will come and feed the children."

"And you?" Raoul said. "How do you think they'll treat you?"

"As a nurse, I'm protected by international law."

"International law! What does law mean to Germans?" Raoul pounded the floor with his cane. "The *boches* aren't getting these youngsters if I can help it!"

"But Raoul, we've no transportation and they can't simply walk away," Justine said.

"Maybe we won't have to budge. Maybe our soldiers will stop the *boches.*" Raoul gestured impatiently. "Ah, I'm talking drivel. They can't beat the Germans. If only we had a big truck. I'd pack the children in it and—no, it's all a dream."

The old man fell silent and stood with his great shaggy head bent in despair. Justine paced back and forth, Berthe wrung her hands and made soft, sobbing sounds. Suddenly Raoul looked up, his brows drawn together, head cocked in a listening attitude.

"Do you hear?" he asked.

"Nothing. Only the surf," the cook said.

"No, no. Motors. Truck motors—" Raoul hobbled to the front door. "The *boches*—"

Berthe let out a stifled scream. Justine drew herself stiffly erect. She straightened her uniform and poked at her hair.

"Berthe, tell Marie to bring the children upstairs." she ordered.

Berthe nodded and skittered down the hallway with a clatter of nervous footsteps.

"So, Raoul." Justine smiled. "The problem is out of our hands."

"Aye. I hope the *boches* still have some humanity left."

"They'll be kind to the children."

"We'll soon find out," Raoul said and limped towards the door.

"Where are you going?" Justine asked.

"To meet them on the road."

Justine stepped up to him and placed a hand on his arm. "Raoul, please, don't do anything foolish."

"You mean fight? I'm an old man. Don't fret. I'll greet them with a bow and a smile." Raoul opened the door and glanced up at the sky. "A nice afternoon," he said. "A very nice afternoon."

He walked out.

# 5

Justine listened to the oncoming trucks with growing dread. Perhaps she should not have insisted on staying at *La Maison*. She should have listened to Raoul and fled with the children that first morning. They could have been safe in France by now. But it was too late for regrets. The *boches* were at hand.

Seconds later the children trooped noisily upstairs, followed by Marie and Berthe. Justine reluctantly prepared to tell them what was in store.

She clapped her hands for attention. "Line up quickly, *mes enfants*. You must listen closely to what I am about to say."

After some milling about, the youngsters stood in uneven ranks, the smallest in front. Berthe was sniffling into a balled handkerchief while Marie blinked hard to hold back her tears.

The trucks were very close, their motors throbbing. Before Justine could speak, the children sensed the truth. A whisper rustled among them like a breeze riffling autumn leaves. *"Les boches! Les boches!"*

The whisper was repeated until it became a frantic shout. The children ran crying to Justine as the trucks stopped on the road.

Heavy footsteps crunched on the gravel path. Justine spoke softly to the sobbing youngsters. "We must all be brave. Please stop crying. Show them we Belgians are brave."

Somehow her quiet words worked. Georges called out, "Come on, little ones. Get in line. We won't let the *boches* see us crying, will we?"

Quickly the children formed two rows. Tears still glistened on smudged faces, lips quivered and chins trembled, but the small bodies were erect with quiet dignity.

*"Merci, mes enfants,"* Justine said.

The footsteps were outside the door and she moved protectively toward the children. Marie was standing with the six-year-olds, her face pale and drawn, while Berthe, cheeks flaming red, bony fists clenched, waited at the end of the line.

The big door swung open. Raoul was there, grinning broadly and swinging his cane like a baton. "Madame! We're saved!" he shouted gleefully.

Behind him, wearing a rumpled Belgian army major's uniform, a pistol strapped around his bulging waist, was a sweat-stained, bearded man. Two armed soldiers waited outside.

Justine blinked at the major. "Monsieur Mercier!" she cried. "We thought—"

"Never mind that," Mercier interrupted. "The Government has left Brussels and gone to Ostend. I'm to take all of you there. You must hurry. The trucks are waiting."

Justine directed Berthe and Marie. "Go with the children, at once."

"Yes, yes, quickly, quickly," Mercier said. "The Germans—" He mopped his brow with a grimy handkerchief and called out to the soldiers. "Get the children aboard the trucks without delay."

The youngsters filed out of *La Maison,* flanked by the soldiers. Marie, holding a little girl's hand led the column, while Berthe brought up the rear. Raoul, Mercier and Justine remained in the château.

Mercier waved a pudgy hand. "I'd have come for you sooner but it wasn't easy to get trucks or drivers. Are you ready, Justine?"

"I'll get my first-aid kit," she said.

"Good," Mercier agreed. "We may need it."

She hurried to her office and reached up on the shelf for the worn black leather bag which held her medical gear. She curled her fingers around the handle, gripping it tightly.

The bag gave her the reassurance that at least something familiar remained. The soft leather handle felt to her touch as it had through all the years. She turned to go, but paused for a final glance at the office, the dingy room where she had spent so many hours wrapped in work and worry.

As she stood there, Justine realized that *La Maison* no longer existed. Without the children the château was merely an old stone house dying on a hillside. Perhaps the Germans would blow it to bits; she hoped it would be given such an end. Better for it to go at once in smoke and flame than to rot piece by piece, a deserted, neglected hulk.

She turned and fled down the corridor. Raoul and Mercier awaited her in the entrance way. "I'm ready," she panted.

"All right, let's get out of here," Mercier said, glancing anxiously at the sky. "The *boches* might show up any minute." He took the bag from Justine and holding her arm, hurried her down the path. Raoul came limping after them.

Two army trucks, facing west, were parked at the roadside, their motors running. Marie and the younger children were crowded in the back of the leading truck; Berthe was with the rest, jammed into the second vehicle. Mercier handed Justine the kit and helped her into the cab of the rear truck alongside the driver.

"You'll be all right here," he said. He turned to Raoul and pointed to the first truck. "Squeeze in with the children."

Raoul climbed over the tailgate. When he was settled, Mercier got in the cab next to the driver. Poking his head out the window, he shouted, "Move out! *En avant!*"

His truck pulled ahead in a clash of gears, closely followed by the other. Justine turned in her seat for a last look at *La Maison*. She noticed with a pang that the front door gaped open; it seemed a mark of disrespect to have left the house without properly securing it. The door swung forlornly in the breeze as though protesting this act of neglect from those who had been sheltered within its walls.

# 6

The two trucks jolted away from Heyst and headed for Ostend, about 40 kilometers to the west on the coast, where the Belgian government had fled because the *panzers* were closing in on Brussels. The young soldier-truckdriver told Justine about the destruction of Rotterdam and the Dutch surrender. He appeared resigned to eventual defeat.

"We can't stop the *boches* even with the Tommies and *poilus*. There's no hope," he said gloomily. "I'm glad the major picked me for this detail. If I wasn't driving you, I'd be back there some place, getting my head shot off by the *panzers*."

The situation was even more critical than the driver knew. As the trucks sped along the bomb-pocked road, fast-moving German tank columns raced into Abbeville, on France's Channel coast, cutting off thousands of British, French and Belgian troops in a vast pocket. At the same time, the masses of Belgian civilians fleeing toward France along the coastal road were also trapped, their escape route slashed by the Germans.

Adding to the confusion, many French peasants,

villagers and townsmen in the Pas de Calais area, made homeless by *Luftwaffe* bombings and unable to head south, where the Nazis were, wandered the roads leading to the Belgian border. Soon a great collision of French and Belgian refugees was inevitable. Nazi planes kept the human mass on the move like herds of cattle.

British, French and Belgians—hampered by civilian-choked roads—tried to make a stand and form a consolidated front, but failed. If they checked the Germans at one point, the enemy broke through elsewhere and the exhausted Allies staggered back to the Channel ports—Calais, Boulogne and Dunkerque. Almost 800,000 Allied soldiers, including the entire British Expeditionary Force (B.E.F.), the Belgian army and remnants of the French First, Seventh and Ninth Armies, were trapped north of Abbeville together with nearly 1,000,000 civilians.

Having captured Abbeville at the mouth of the Somme River, the Germans now headed for the big ports of Calais and Boulogne. The French and British fought to hold these cities, but the Nazis drew the strangling noose tighter. Battles raged day and night with an intensity never before known in modern warfare. The ear-splitting noise of bombing and shelling, the constant chatter of rifles and machine guns, drowned out the death rattle in the throat of Europe.

The route to Ostend was a highway of terror. Craters gaped in the road; truncated trees, splintered by bomb fragments and machine-gun bullets, lined the road on both sides. Wrecked cars, wagons and trucks, some still smoldering, were strewn about. A young woman sprawled dead in a ditch, where strafing bullets had caught her. A few yards farther on lay three more bodies. Every foot of the way bore its grisly memento of the Nazi aerial *blitz*.

For a short time after leaving *La Maison,* the two trucks kept up a fair speed, but as the road became more cluttered, they were forced to slow down. The refugees had covered only 15 kilometers when dusk came on. As daylight faded, Justine could hardly see the first truck, only twenty yards ahead, through the smoke haze rising from burning cars and other vehicles.

Worried about the children, she peered through the isinglass window of the curtain that separated the cab from the rear of the truck. In the gloomy half-light, she saw them packed one against the other on the floor and the two drop benches. As though drugged, they had fallen into a deep sleep, heads rolling limply and arms dangling with each motion of the truck.

As darkness closed in, the driver's boyish features twisted anxiously. "We won't make Ostend today. It's getting too dark and we can't use headlights," he muttered.

"You mean we'll have to stop?" Justine asked in dismay.

"Can't go much farther, madame. We'd crack up on this road." The driver shrugged.

A flashlight winked from the cab of the first truck. "That's it," Justine's chauffeur said. "The major's signaling me to pull over."

He eased the big vehicle to the side of the road. The other truck had already parked. Mercier came trudging back in the deepening darkness.

He opened the door of the cab. "It's too dangerous to continue," he announced. "We can camp over there." He gestured toward a broad, open field.

Justine nodded glumly. She had counted on reaching Ostend that night. The authorities there surely would have facilities for the children, at least food and shelter. But long ago she had learned to make the best of things.

While the prospect of spending the night in the open was not a pleasing one, at least the weather was balmy and stars twinkled overhead. In other circumstances, sleeping out on such a night would have been fun. Justine loved the outdoors. As a schoolgirl, she had often spent her holidays bicycling across Belgium and France with her classmates, camping in fields and woods.

The children snapped awake when the truck stopped. Heads popped out over the truck tailgate and a hundred questions were thrown into the dark.

"Everybody out, we're staying the night," Mercier called.

The young passengers clambered down. Tearfully complaining that they were sleepy, hungry, thirsty and scared, they lined up two-by-two and stumbled into the field to a grove about a hundred yards away. When they reached the trees, Mercier addressed everyone.

"I am sorry there is nothing to eat. We leave at dawn for Ostend where I promise you'll be fed. Now everybody get some sleep."

The children obeyed him. The ground was padded by grass and many layers of fallen leaves. Each child burrowed into the soft bed and soon enough fell fast asleep.

Justine tried to stay awake but she dozed, propped against a tree. Nearby, Marie slept soundly, with Berthe next to her. Somewhere, a night bird called, an owl hooted and flew off with a flutter of wings. A match glowed in the blackness, its flame illuminating Raoul's bearded face as he lit his pipe. He stood at the edge of the woods, puffing on the pipe and studying the sky. Mercier came toward him from the deep shadows cast by the trees. The official wearily pressed fingertips against his eyes.

"I'm exhausted," he said hoarsely. "I'd like a glass of good cognac."

"You're not the only one," Raoul said.

"Only last week I was in Brussels at a concert.

Who would have believed—" Mercier sighed. He drew a cigar from his blouse pocket. "My last one." He shrugged and lit the cigar, drawing in its fragrance appreciatively. "This war. We're lost, Raoul. Lost!"

The old man stood silently, puffing his pipe. At last he said, "What will be, will be. It's no good brooding over something that can't be changed." He knocked the dottle out of his pipe and said, "I'm going to turn in. *Bon soir,* monsieur."

"*Bon soir,* Raoul." Mercier stood alone, smoking the cigar. He stared into the darkness, his thick body sagging. There was no trace of the pompous politician he had once been. Now he was only a fat man in a crumpled army uniform facing an uncertain tomorrow.

# 7

Thursday, May 16, dawned without promise. Dirty gray clouds scudded in from the sea. A brisk wind came to chill the boys and girls sleeping on the ground. They awoke in stiff discomfort to the cheerless morning. This was a dawn that throttled hope, a disgruntled day suitable only for harsh words and bad tempers.

Justine awakened feeling as though she had aged twenty years overnight. She stretched to relieve her cramped muscles. Marie and Berthe also stirred into wakefulness.

"Oh, God, I'm broken in half," Berthe grumbled. "I slept on a rock with sharp points."

Marie smiled, running fingers through her tangled blonde hair. "Don't complain, Berthe. I was lying on the same rock, or one like it."

A drizzle started to fall. It was more wet mist than rain. Justine looked up at the leaden sky. "That's all we need. A wet day. Half our children will be sick before nightfall."

"Those poor lambs, doing without breakfast," Berthe moaned. "They need porridge and hot milk."

"So do we all." Justine forced a laugh. "Cheer up. We'll soon be in Ostend and our troubles will be over."

"Oh, madame. It's awful. We're like gypsies, without a home." Berthe began to sniffle.

Justine patted the cook's bony shoulder. "Now, now. Pull yourself together. Do you want the children to see you crying?"

"Oh, no." Berthe struggled to swallow a sob. "There, I'll be all right now. But I do wish we had porridge for them."

"You'd solve the world's problems with porridge, eh, Berthe?" Justine teased.

"Why not? Mine is a better way than this," Berthe replied.

Mercier came toward them, bedraggled and disarrayed, his officer's cap at an angle, his blouse unbuttoned. The pistol slapped against his hip with each step.

"We'll be moving out in five minutes," he said.

"Please get the children ready," Justine said to Berthe and Marie. The two women left. Mercier eyed her unhappily. He fumbled for words, then blurted out, "Forgive me—please—you must—"

"Forgive you? For what?"

"I'm not a cold, indifferent politician. I care about the youngsters, you can see that. I came for them, didn't I? But I couldn't squeeze out more money for *La Maison*. I had to move cautiously. I wanted a high post in the government—I—" He twisted his hands helplessly.

"I understand, Charles. Your ambitions were important to you."

"Justine, that's not it."

She gestured toward the children clustered miserably beneath the dripping trees. "I'm not blaming you, Charles. Perhaps all this could have been prevented, perhaps not. We've no time for talk. The children must get to Ostend before they all catch pneumonia."

Mercier squared his shoulders. "Yes. I'll see you at the trucks."

The children formed a column and came out of the grove to the trucks. It was raining steadily when they pulled away. For the first time since fleeing Heyst, traffic almost stopped them. They overtook stragglers, old men and women, bent under heavy bundles. As the trucks approached, the refugees silently implored a ride. But when the vehicles swept past, they went on again, eyes dull with despair, still clutching their burdens—chattels of the dispossessed: blankets, pillows, mattresses, pots, pans, a sewing machine, a baby's crib.

No strangers to war, some of them had traveled the same cruel road before. In 1914 their land had been ravaged, cottages razed and livestock slaughtered. Stoically they faced the new disasters as though such troubles were an accepted part of life.

The trucks made slow progress toward Ostend. Drivers cursed, horns blared and the traffic grew thicker. Thousands of people on foot pushed through open fields, fording streams and stumbling across marshy places.

Families were separated in the great press. Mothers screamed for lost children, husbands frantically searched for their wives. The cries, shouts, screams and sobs added to the confusion. Amid all this, Belgian, French and British infantrymen, rifles slung, slogged in the opposite direction. A tank column forced a passage through the crowd.

Soldiers were digging foxholes and machine-gun emplacements in the fields. Here and there, anti-aircraft guns poked long barrels skyward. On every side were marks of earlier *Luftwaffe* attacks: dead cattle, burned farmhouses and barns, debris, wreckage and rubble.

The trucks carrying the children drifted with the choked traffic. They rolled no more than a few yards in almost an hour. The long delays irked Justine. She peered fretfully through the rivulets running down the windshield as the wipers swayed in cadence like twin metronomes. As far as she could see, the road was blocked by vehicles.

During one halt the driver, reaching for a cigarette, found only an empty pack. He crumpled and flung it vehemently against the windshield.

"No cigarettes," he cried. "Damn it! Why don't we move?"

Justine smiled wanly. "Please don't shout."

"I'm sorry, madame," the driver said. "I'm all nerves."

Justine sighed and glanced out of the cab window at a peasant family stumbling by in the rain. The woman, gray-faced with fatigue, was pushing a baby carriage on which a sopping wet bundle of bedding perched precariously. Her husband walked by her side carrying a five- or six-year-old boy wrapped in a dripping blanket.

"Those poor souls out there," Justine remarked. "I wish it would stop raining for their sake."

"Don't say that. The rain's the only good luck we've had. It's keeping the *Stukas* on the ground. I hope it rains forever," the driver said.

But the downpour ended at about 1 P.M. and a brilliant sun shone from a cloudless sky. The refugees looked aloft apprehensively. Anti-aircraft gunners searched for Nazi planes and mass tension verging on panic spread through the throng.

Somewhere, kilometers away, the bottleneck that had clogged traffic unexpectedly opened. All at once there was a forward surge and the vehicles began to move steadily. Gendarmes and military policemen appeared at crossroads to wave the cars on. No one knew or cared how this had come about. Everybody had only one concern, not to be caught on that road by the *Luftwaffe*.

Justine's driver followed the truck ahead, swerving to keep from crashing into other cars or hitting pedestrians. The lorry rocked like a boat caught in a North Sea squall. Justine, clinging to the cab's hand-strap, heard the children in the rear screaming as the movement of the speeding truck tossed them about roughly.

It was a wild and grotesque race along that road. Bicyclists pedaled furiously. Horses pulling farm carts and wagons were whipped to a gallop by frenzied drivers. The foam-flecked animals charged ahead with eyes bulging, nostrils flaring and flanks heaving.

In the carts and wagons, frightened riders hung on for their lives. Bruised and shaken, they were thrown violently from side to side. A wagon turned over, spilling its passengers into the drainage ditch. They lay bleeding there, amid scattered belongings, while the horse galloped on, still dragging the up-ended wagon.

People on foot broke into a run, dropping the bundles they had carried so long and so far. They spread out across the muddy fields. No pedestrian dared keep to the road among all the fast-moving vehicles.

As though taken from some grossly comic nightmare, a fat man waddled through ankle-deep mud in a desperate effort to run. He stumbled and fell face down in the muck.

A tall teen-aged girl, holding a baby in her arms, ran with graceful, long-legged strides, her corn-silk hair billowing out like a golden net.

So they ran: the young with lithe, sure steps, the old in pathetic imitation of them. But it was an unequal race. Shortly after the rain had ended, six *Stuka* dive bombers took off from a combat airstrip about 140 kilometers to the east. The flight leader's orders were to bomb and strafe the Ostend road.

About an hour later, the *Stukas* reached the target. The leader pulled up for his dive and the other planes followed close behind. At his signal they lanced down out of the sun, noses pointed toward the road below and the fields dotted with people. The flight leader pushed the firing button of his machine guns. He watched the red line of tracers streaking earthward to the scurrying figures in the fields.

The bullets kicked up spurts of mud until a burst caught the tall blonde girl in mid-stride. She froze for a split-second like a splendid statue and then spun around to drop spread-eagled in the mud. The baby fell unscathed, its wailing unnoticed as the planes swooped down like birds of prey. Fear-maddened refugees fled in all directions; many tumbled to the ground, cut down by the machine guns.

# 8

In the speeding truck, Justine was not aware of
the air attack until the *Stukas* straddled the road
with bombs. Explosions rocked the vehicle and
shrapnel clanged against its sides. Smoke blotted the
truck ahead from her sight.

"My God!" Justine screamed. "They've been hit!"

Cursing, the driver yanked hard on the wheel,
sending the truck in a sharp turn to the opposite side
of the road. "I knew it! I knew it! That damned
*Luftwaffe!*" he cried.

"The children!" Justine had no other thought.
"Stop! I must go to the children."

"They haven't been touched! Look there," the
driver yelled, fighting to control the vehicle.

The smoke thinned out and through the haze,
Justine saw that the first truck was also zigzagging at
top speed. She glimpsed an automobile burning and
bodies lying near the wreck. Grisly sights wove a
tapestry of horror. Watching it unfold so swiftly
deadened the impact on Justine; the aftermath of
the bombing numbed rather than shocked her.

The *Stukas* were not yet finished. They swung in

a wide circle and came around again for a strafing run. But this time they met with unexpected resistance. A British machine-gun section dug in amid the rubble of a farmhouse opened fire on the planes. The Nazi flight leader's ship was hit; with smoke pouring from its fuselage, the *Stuka* crashed in a field and exploded.

Justine's driver gave a gleeful shout. "Good! Good! That's one less *boche!*" he cheered.

The remaining German bombers pressed the attack. Their tracer bullets crisscrossed the road. Cars were hit and people killed, but the two truckloads of children were untouched. At last the Nazi planes, running low on fuel and ammunition, turned back.

After the *Stukas* left, the way was clear to Ostend. That port city bore the scars of German air raids; many buildings were damaged and smoke hung over the dock area where fires had been burning for several days. Hundreds of refugees, seeking food and shelter, wandered the streets.

Despite all the destruction, order still prevailed in Ostend. Troops were on patrol; anti-aircraft batteries stood guard; the outskirts of the city were protected by tanks, artillery and infantry.

The trucks rolled into the city about 3 P.M. and finally stopped at a red-brick building, a furniture factory that had been converted to serve as military headquarters. The Belgian flag fluttered from the roof, its black, yellow and red stripes bright in the afternoon sun. Sentries paced at the entrance and machine guns covered the approaches. Mercier descended from his cab and walked stiffly to Justine. His unshaven face was haggard, beefy jowls quivering loosely. He looked old and spent.

"Are you all right, Justine?" he asked, opening the door.

"Never mind me. The children—"

"They'll be looked after."

Mercier helped Justine climb from the cab. She stood swaying, knees buckling, and Mercier steadied her.

"I'm fine, now," she said. "Please, Charles, see to the children."

"Of course. Help the children out of the trucks," Mercier ordered the drivers. He beckoned to some soldiers grouped near the headquarters. "Lend a hand, men."

"Yes, sir," a sergeant said. "You heard him," he snapped at his companions.

Mercier pointed to a building about half a block away. A Red Cross flag was flapping over the doorway and the roof bore a huge Red Cross painted on white canvas.

"There's the medical station, Justine," Mercier said. "Take the children there."

"They need food, Charles."

"And they'll have it," Mercier promised. He turned to the sergeant. "See them to the station.

Give Madame Raymond all the assistance you can."

"Yes, sir," the sergeant said, saluting.

Mercier returned his salute. "I'll join you as soon as possible, Justine," he said and entered the headquarters building.

The truck tailboards were lowered and the soldiers assisted the frightened, hungry children out of the trucks. A few could hardly stand, let alone walk. These the soldiers carried as the group filed toward the medical station. Berthe and Marie, each leading a child by the hand, stayed at the head of the column while Justine and Raoul brought up the rear.

The old man, limping badly, leaned heavily on his cane. "Slammed my leg against the side of the truck," he grumbled.

"Does it hurt much?" Justine asked.

"Enough," he said. He paused for a moment and glanced around. "This town took a pounding. We seem to be neither better nor worse off than before."

"Perhaps if we can stay here in Ostend for a few days it would be possible to have the children rejoin their parents. Mercier says—"

"Who believes politicians anyway? They got us into this in the first place. There isn't one, madame, not one, who's not a born liar!"

"Raoul! You're unfair."

"What's fair to do with it? Facts are facts. The *boche* tanks are coming down from Holland. They're pushing west across Belgium and we're cut off from the south. We don't have a few days here. We'll be lucky if we're not on the run again tomorrow."

"You make things sound black, Raoul."

"That's the truth, no matter how Mercier tells it. The *boches* have us in a net—Belgians, Tommies, French, Dutch—flopping about like a catch of North Sea herring, while they haul us in."

Justine stopped and gripped the old man's arm. "No, it mustn't end like that! There's surely some way out."

Raoul drew his shaggy brows together. "Yes, madame, there is." He jerked a thumb in the direction of the sea. "Over the water to England."

"England? And how are we supposed to get there?"

"Put the youngsters aboard a cross-Channel steamer and take them to England before it's too late."

"That's impossible without orders from the committee. I can't simply leave with fifty children."

"Red tape! That's all! Red tape! Politicians! Bah!" Raoul snarled. "It's just common sense. If you want to save the little ones from the Nazis, go to England!"

"I'll ask Monsieur Mercier. You don't have to respect Charles, but I'm obliged to obey his orders. If he thinks it best to evacuate the children to England,

I'll do it. If not, we'll stay in Belgium or keep on to France."

"All right, madame. I've had my say. Just remember it was old Raoul who told you how to save the children."

"Raoul, Raoul, you're like a grouchy old bear." Justine smiled.

"I don't mean to growl at you, madame, but there's so little time left. In two, three days at the most, the *boches* will pick us up like rabbits."

"Things can change for the better, even in a few days. Remember how the Germans were stopped at the Marne in 1914? Maybe we'll have another such military miracle."

"I don't believe in miracles."

"You should have more faith."

Raoul gripped his stick more tightly. "We're talking in circles, madame. I know you can't run away to England, just like that. I'm sure Mercier can give you a thousand reasons for staying; I have only one for going—the Germans."

Justine patted his arm. "I'll speak to Monsieur Mercier, I promise. But we can't decide anything now so let's get to the medical station. They'll be wondering what's happened to us."

# 9

The thick-walled, two-story brick building which housed the medical station once had been a paint warehouse. The structure was of such sturdy construction that a pair of bomb hits had done only superficial damage, breaking the windows which were now boarded up.

The ground floor was crowded with rows of canvas cots, set up only inches apart; wounded soldiers and civilians occupied them. Harried nurses and orderlies went from one patient to another; doctors in soiled white coats treated the injured.

The room was poorly lighted by naked electric bulbs dangling on drop wires. Their stark glow cast distorted shadows which paraded along the walls in a procession of weird shapes.

The air in that makeshift hospital reeked of carbolic, blood, sweat, burned flesh, tobacco smoke, the mingling of a dozen unpleasant odors. There was never a still moment, never an instant of silence. Wounded groaned and cried out; doctors called to nurses. It was a bedlam of noise, pain and death. Added to all the tumult and confusion were tearful refugees clamoring for food and shelter. Only the wounded were admitted; armed guards drove the rest away, often with violence.

When the children from *La Maison* appeared, they were let in without delay. A soldier guided them up a rickety flight of wooden stairs to the upper floor where a temporary kitchen had been set up at one end of an immense loft. Cooks, enshrouded in clouds of steam that rose from two huge cauldrons simmering on the stove, dished out a bowl of soup and a thick slab of army bread to each child. This was devoured at crude tables that ran along both walls.

While the children were eating, a detail of soldiers placed canvas army cots at the far side of the enormous room. With their hunger sated by the soup and bread, the weary children stumbled to the cots and were soon fast asleep.

Justine stretched out on a cot. Weariness gnawed at her bones; every muscle ached. Around her she heard the breathing of the exhausted sleepers. A squad of infantrymen clumped up the stairs to the kitchen and were served. Mess kits clattered and equipment rattled as the soldiers ate and talked in low voices.

Justine closed her eyes, but could not sleep. Everything that had happened in the last tumultuous week unreeled before her in unrelated segments. She saw again the horror on the road to Ostend;

blood spurting from sudden, gaping wounds; *Stuka* machine guns; the red-orange flash of exploding bombs.

And in this welter she thought again of Marcel, worrying about his safety, whispering a prayer for him. Tears burned her eyes and she was overwhelmed by a wave of great sadness, a feeling of loneliness.

She saw herself on a vast and treeless plain, where the fierce sun baked the earth and where nothing grew except stunted brush. Wispy grass patches were sere and scorched as though a giant white-hot flame had passed over that land.

She walked across this wide barren tract, growing weaker with each step. At last, unable to move, she sank to the parched earth. The sun, a bright, blinding glare, blazed in her eyes.

And from a distance a voice called her name. She sat upright, blinking in the beam of an electric torch, dully aware that she had been asleep and dreaming. Shielding her eyes from the flashlight, she spoke to the shadowy figure holding it.

"Who's there?" she asked.

"Charles. I'm sorry to awaken you, Justine, but this is urgent." Mercier's voice quavered with tension.

Justine closed her eyes for a moment. Sleepers were stirring on every side. One child coughed;

another groaned. There was restless thrashing and movement and she sensed the uneasy disquiet.

Swinging her legs off the cot, Justine looked at Mercier, who loomed in bulky silhouette.

"What is it, Charles?" she asked, guessing the answer.

"The Germans are closing in on Ostend. The government people have started to pull out. I wangled trucks for you and the children. Get ready to move in twenty minutes," Mercier said.

Justine listened to him with detachment, as though his words did not really concern her. She felt neither fear nor anxiety; her reaction was resignation to an inevitable doom. She sat silently, head bowed, in an attitude of prayer.

"Did you hear me, Justine?" Mercier whispered irritably. "The Germans—"

"I heard, Charles." She shrugged and rose heavily. For a moment she stood looking at the sleepers huddled on the cots and grieved for them as one mourns the dead.

"Justine, for heaven's sake, pull yourself together," Mercier said. "The trucks are waiting."

"Yes, Charles, the trucks." She swung around and faced him. "And where are we going?"

"The Government is setting up across the French border at Dunkerque, they say. You are to go there."

"Charles, the Germans will get Dunkerque too.

It will only be a matter of a few days. Then where do we go? These children can't take much more."

"You can't stay here! That's all I know," Mercier said in an anguished voice.

"Will you arrange for a boat that could take us to England?"

Mercier gestured impatiently. "Impossible! The docks are a shambles. It's either the trucks to Dunkerque or the Germans."

"I'll wake the children," Justine said. "What time is it?"

Mercier flicked on the light and glanced at his watch. "Half past four. You have twenty minutes."

As he was about to leave, a dull explosion thudded outside. It sounded like a heavy door slamming in the distance. Mercier paused, cocked his head and listened. Another door slammed, then another, then a swift succession of them.

"Artillery," Mercier said. "The *boches* are shelling our positions outside of town."

The explosions jarred the children awake. They sat wide-eyed and frightened; a little girl screamed for her mother and the shrill cries electrified Justine into action.

"Berthe! Marie! Look after the children! We're leaving here, now!" Glancing at Mercier, she said, "Send the trucks, Charles, we'll be ready."

Mercier nodded and hurried out. The shelling became severe; it seemed closer to Justine. She reached under the cot for the first-aid bag as Raoul stomped to her side.

"Are we pulling out?" he asked.

"Yes, for Dunkerque."

"How about the boat to England?"

"Impossible."

"Who says so? Mercier?"

"Raoul, the Germans are coming. Please, let's not argue."

"Run, little rabbits. Run, run, run. But there's no escaping the fox that's chasing us, no matter how fast we run," he said.

# 10

By the time the two army trucks rolled up to the medical station, Justine was waiting with the children who stood docilely against a wall, shocked into passivity. Even when shells came crashing in nearby streets, they showed little reaction, except to move closer together, taking comfort from one another.

All Ostend was astir, brought to life by the shelling. Armored cars, weapons carriers and trucks rolled by at breakneck speed. Foot soldiers, shadowy in the lightening darkness, hurried to the northern section of the city where rifle and machine-gun fire sounded amid thudding shells.

Civilians ran into the street without purpose, from one point to another. In the station the patients were terrified; badly wounded men begged to be helped from their cots; those able to, dragged themselves out of the building, which offered shelter, into the street where death menaced.

Mercier leaped from a truck and shouted, "Get them aboard! Hurry!" But as the children were being led to the vehicles, a shell crashed into an adjacent building. Shrapnel, bricks and stone fragments rained down.

"Get down!" Raoul cried hoarsely, flinging himself to the pavement and pulling two children with him.

The truck drivers and Mercier also dropped prone, but they were the only ones who did so. Justine stood frozen, gripping her medical bag, staring with disbelief as a wall of the struck building collapsed, hurling more debris into the street.

Within seconds, another shell landed across the street. The blast tore a deep hole in the pavement. Jagged metal and chips of paving block whistled through the air. The concussion knocked children off their feet.

A chunk of metal caught Marie between the shoulder blades. The impact flung her against the wall of the medical station. Berthe, lifted bodily, was slammed to the pavement with stunning force. Thrown to her knees, Justine remained in a kneeling position. Shrapnel shredded the canvas roofs of the trucks and dented their metal sides. A windshield was shattered on one vehicle; the headlights smashed on the other, its motor hood dented by falling debris.

Even as the second shell was exploding, a third dropped further down the street, away from the medical station. The shelling moved on to another district of Ostend.

Justine rose slowly to her feet. She expected to find only mangled corpses; but one by one the others got to their feet, shaken and dazed, but alive and unhurt. Only Marie lay motionless.

Raoul spied her first and hobbled to the girl's side. He turned her over and in the gray light of approaching dawn, saw at a glance that she was dead. Justine was there a moment later.

"Oh, God! Marie!" she exclaimed.

Raoul rose from the body. His fingers were blood-stained. The children, who had formed a half-circle, stared at the slain girl lying in the rubble.

"Get the children aboard the trucks!" Raoul shouted, gesturing at them.

With the help of the drivers, the children were placed in the vehicles. Justine and Raoul lingered over Marie for a few moments. Justine wept silently; Raoul stood stricken, leaning on his cane. Mercier bustled to them.

"Time to move," he said. "They're all aboard."

Raoul placed a big, gnarled hand on Justine's shoulder and patted her gently. "Come, we can do no good here."

He led Justine to a truck and helped her into the cab. Tear-stained, she looked at him. "Marie was so young, so very young to die," she sobbed.

"Nobody's ever old enough," Raoul said. He slammed the door and limped toward the rear of the vehicle. He was about to climb over the tailgate when Mercier took his arm and pointed to the cab of the second truck. "You're riding with the driver," he said.

"That's your seat, isn't it?" Raoul asked.

"I'm not going," Mercier said. "I've been ordered to stay with the rear guard. They need a field-grade officer."

"You?"

"Why not? I wasn't always what you call a 'bureaucrat.' King Albert pinned a medal on me back in 1918. For heroism." Mercier smiled. "Don't be so surprised, old man, people aren't always as they seem. Go on now, get moving."

"Monsieur Mercier—" Raoul began. He stopped and thrust out his hand. "Good luck."

Mercier gripped his hand. "Thanks. But nothing matters for me anymore. My wife and daughter were killed by a bomb yesterday. Headquarters had it over the military radio from Brussels." Mercier tugged at his pistol belt. "So I volunteered for the rear guard. I hope to get a *boche* or two."

The rifle and machine-gun fire to the north intensified. Both men turned in that direction. "The *boches* are knocking at the door. I must join the welcoming committee. Say *au revoir* to Justine for me." Mercier strode away, without a backward glance, toward a group of soldiers standing near the headquarters building.

Raoul watched him go. For the first time he did

not see Mercier as a grasping politician, but a man both base and noble; weak and strong; cowardly and brave; a human being.

Raoul limped to the truck, swung up beside the driver and slammed shut the door. The two trucks lurched away, heading south for the French border. As the vehicles swung around in the shell-pitted street, Justine turned for a last look at Marie. The dead girl reminded her of a broken doll flung carelessly aside.

One side of the main road from Ostend was crowded with now familiar masses of civilian refugees moving southward; on the other side, troops marched in double file, heading towards the port city. The units were mixed: French Foreign Legionnaires in sky-blue uniforms followed Belgian infantrymen, while British Tommies marched behind the French.

The mud-stained, battle-weary troops were survivors of decimated regiments, brigades and even divisions which had vainly been trying to hold the Germans in a week of relentless combat. Separated from their own commands, the soldiers had gathered in small groups, even as individuals, and reorganized by nationality to continue fighting.

They were making a last-ditch stand to hold the ports north of Abbeville, especially Ostend, Dunkerque, Calais and Boulogne. These were vital, as avenues of supply and possible escape for the Allied armies caught in the German entrapment. If the Nazis took all ports, the British Expeditionary Force was doomed to annihilation or capture, as were the French and Belgian forces.

The Allies were slowly being pushed into an ever dwindling area and the men knew they had only a forlorn hope of breaking the steel cordon the *Wehrmacht* had thrown around them. Beaten, but not routed, the Allied soldiers fought with desperate bravery.

Inadequately armed and often badly led, the British, French and Belgians struggled valiantly. They were hamstrung by poor strategy, hidebound thinking in high places, obsolete equipment and outmoded tactics.

Despite these handicaps, they inflicted heavy losses on the enemy, casualties far greater than Hitler and his generals had anticipated. Code Yellow was going well for the Germans, but thousands of their best shock troops were being sacrificed for Hitler's Third Reich.

All through Germany, even as victory bells pealed, more and still more people with mourning armbands appeared on the streets. Crepe hung on the doors of peasant cottages and city townhouses. Germans were learning that the *Fuehrer,* who had vowed to lead the Fatherland into a thousand years of glory, demanded a high price for his ambitions— the blood, lives and strength of Germany's youth.

# 11

Dunkerque, about 50 kilometers southwest of Ostend, had a population of some 35,000 in 1940. It was the first good-sized French town across the Belgian border which lay less than 20 kilometers to the north.

The fourth most important seaport of France, Dunkerque had a fine harbor, capable of handling the largest ships; its piers and quays stretched for almost five miles along the waterfront and were among the best equipped in all Europe. A commercial hub, Dunkerque was the terminus of many canals cutting through industrial northern France and Belgium. Ships of all flags brought products to Dunkerque and carried away chalk, phosphate, iron ore, coal, chemicals and metals from French and Belgian mines.

Prosperous and well-kept, the city had broad, paved streets which converged on a wide square, *Place Jean Bart,* named for a French naval hero born at Dunkerque in 1651. His statue stood in the center of the *Place.* Nearby rose the 290-foot-high belfry of the Church of St. Eloi whose world-renowned bells attracted many tourists. Long a noted cultural center, Dunkerque had a college, a school of drawing, architecture and music, and a museum which held many masterpieces. Thousands of rare manuscripts and books reposed in its library.

Malo-les-Bains, a popular bathing resort, was only a kilometer to the northeast. In summer its white sands were crowded with tourists from all over Europe. Malo-les-Bains was a particular favorite of English visitors, who crossed the Straits of Dover by the hundreds on the daily Dover-Dunkerque ferry.

While the truck nosed along the crowded highway, Justine recalled her many visits to Malo-les-Bains and Dunkerque. As a child, she had spent the summer holidays there with her parents and brothers in a rented seaside cottage. The last time the whole family had been together at Malo-les-Bains was during the summer of 1914; she remembered clearly the hot July days when Europe seethed with war rumors after a Serbian student assassinated Archduke Franz Ferdinand of Austria at Sarajevo.

Everybody talked about war that July; the men sat on the sand, puffing their cigars, arguing, explaining, discussing. Justine remembered her father tracing a map in the sand with a pointed stick, jabbing at it here and there to explain some strategy.

She understood little of what was being said; the grownups seemed to be speaking another language filled with such strange words as logistics, mobilization, flanking movements, neutrality, aggression. She did know that the the old Emperor of Austria, Franz Josef, was angry at Serbia and the Russian Czar wanted to aid the Serbs against the Austrians. If he did that, the German Kaiser would fight the Czar and the French were pledged to help the Russians. But what did all that really matter to a ten-year-old girl playing in the sand at Malo-les-Bains under the hot July sun?

In the end, it mattered greatly. Within a month, her father had been killed in action at Liége; soon after, both brothers fell in the fighting around Antwerp. Justine and her mother spent the war years in a refugee camp near Paris.

Malo-les-Bains. So many happy memories—the times there with Marcel after the First War; days in the sun; walks on the beach and along the Dunkerque waterfront, looking at the ships moored there —ships from Brazil and China, the United States and Australia, ships from everywhere in the world.

Marcel and she, sipping apéritifs at a sidewalk café on the *Place Jean Bart,* relaxed and contented, watching the couples strolling in the summer evening. And all around, the scaffolded buildings with workmen busy repairing the damage wrought by German bombs and shells; the *boches* had shattered the roof of St. Eloi and riddled the belfry with shrapnel. The scars of 1914–18 were not healed for ten years.

And now she was going to Dunkerque again. Perhaps in that place where she had known so much happiness, this exodus would come to an end. The children had to be fed, given proper care; it was physically impossible for them to keep on without food and rest.

Justine glanced out the cab window. To the east the sun was rising, tinting the sky with morning colors. As it grew lighter, she could make out great numbers of people in the fields. Some still slept in the shelter of trees; the smoke of small cooking fires rose in countless columns as those fortunate enough to have rations prepared breakfast. The plodding mass trampled young cornstalks and tender shoots of barley; anything edible had been rooted out of the ground, the carefully tended fields stripped bare.

The sun rose higher and with full daylight, the havoc caused by the *Luftwaffe* was plainly seen. No farmhouse stood intact. Splintered timbers poked out of fire-blackened ruins like skeletal fingers.

The bloated carcasses of dead cows, horses and other livestock, with stiffened limbs pointing skyward, were strewn about and the stench of rotting flesh polluted the air. The pastoral countryside was a landscape of horror; the week-long German aerial assault had reduced this fertile region to desolation.

The trucks inched on through small villages

where rubble piles marked houses and dead bodies lay unheeded in the street. Death had grown so commonplace that no one even noticed the corpses. The dismal journey continued past the gutted homes and ruined farms. The refugees kept to their side of the road and the soldiers to theirs. Now and then a few tanks rolled northward or horsedrawn field artillery, relics of another time and another war, careened across the fields.

Justine grew increasingly anxious about the children. They had eaten nothing since the soup and bread in Ostend the previous evening. She feared that those recently recovered from pneumonia and other serious illnesses might suffer a relapse. They needed milk, eggs, meat and rest; this arduous trek could cost them their lives.

Near Nieuport vehicular traffic halted at a military police roadblock. The sector was defended by French troops. A squad of burly military policemen, led by a red-jowled sergeant, pushed through a crowd of pedestrians to the truck in which Justine was riding.

The sergeant opened the door and poked his head into the cab. "Madame Raymond?" he asked politely.

"Yes. I'm Justine Raymond. Is anything wrong?" she said anxiously.

"No, no, madame. Calm yourself," the soldier said. "I'm Sergeant Emile Brunel with Fourth Division headquarters. We had a radio message from Ostend that you were coming. There's hot food waiting for the children."

Justine gave a sigh of relief. They had not been forsaken after all, she thought. Perhaps this was the turning point; an end to all the running. The French sergeant seemed so assured, so confident. The *boches* were going to be stopped; everyone knew the French army was the finest in Europe. The Nazis initially had gained the advantage of surprise, but the French and British were now fully mobilized and the enemy no longer would have everything their way.

Sergeant Brunel jumped onto the runningboard. "I'll guide you to the division command post," he told the driver. "Take the lefthand turn beyond the roadblock."

The truck swung off the main route into an unpaved side road, with the second vehicle close behind. The dirt road was narrow and pitted with bomb craters. It led into a heavily wooded area and the trucks had to move slowly, gears grinding. French soldiers stepped out of the woods to watch the trucks pass.

The trucks bounced along the rutted road, splashed across a hubcap-deep stream and skidded up a mudslick slope. They passed camouflaged antiaircraft batteries and machine-gun positions and riflemen in foxholes.

After driving in the woods for about a kilometer, the trucks reached a small clearing. A divisional flag fluttered from its staff beside the doorway of a stone hunting lodge. Officers and enlisted men moved busily about the place.

Off to one side, among the trees, a fly tent had been pitched and a field kitchen was in operation. Soldiers carrying mess tins shuffled past the kitchen where cooks ladled out steaming food to them.

"Pull over under those trees," the sergeant said to the driver, pointing to a place where other vehicles stood.

Moments later the trucks were parked. Soldiers helped the children to the ground and the youngsters stood in a silent, apathetic group. Raoul came to join Berthe and Justine, leaning heavily on his cane.

"Where is Monsieur Mercier?" Justine asked him. "Weren't you riding in his truck?"

Raoul poked the ground with his cane. "He stayed at Ostend with the rear guard. The poor man had just learned that his wife and daughter had been killed in an air raid."

Justine turned away, fists clenched. War! Lives wasted, hopes and dreams shattered.

A gray-haired officer in a rumpled uniform strode up to her. He bowed stiffly and saluted. "Colonel Pierre Vercours, at your service, madame."

"Your sergeant said there would be food for the children."

"And he was correct. The cooks are waiting for them now."

"You're very kind, Colonel."

Vercours shrugged. "Kind? What is left us but a little kindness?" He glanced at the cloudless sky. "On such a day, war is an even greater abomination. Now, madame, the cooks are waiting."

Soon every child was served a heaping plate of stew. Only when the last one had been fed did Justine take any food for herself. After she had eaten, she went to see Vercours in the hunting lodge.

The officer was seated in a camp chair, smoking a cigar. He stood up when Justine entered. "Have your children been fed?" He smiled.

"Yes, Colonel. Thank you. I think we should be leaving soon."

"So you're bound for Dunkerque. What do you hope to find there?"

"I have to see officials of my government or of the Labor Federation. They must have plans for the children. We can't keep on this way much longer. Three days on the road. A young nurse was killed." Justine's voice quavered and broke. Tears welled in her eyes.

"No tears, madame," Vercours said stiffly. "I can appreciate your ordeal, but tears are no help. Our situation isn't a bright one. The Germans are starting to pinch."

He fell silent, lips pursed in thought. Somewhere a military radio chattered. Soldiers hurried in and out of the lodge. A motorcycle pulled up outside, engine roaring, wheels kicking up a spurt of stones and dust. The small headquarters throbbed with bustling activity.

At last Vercours cleared his throat and eyed Justine seriously. "I wish we could guarantee your safety here but this is no place for civilians, especially children. I suppose Dunkerque is best, after all. The French navy has taken control of the city. My friend, Admiral Henri Platon, is the commandant. You'll find his headquarters in the customs house—if it's still standing. I must warn you—Dunkerque has been heavily bombed and will be hit again. I'll give you a note to Platon and also try to reach him by radio. I'm certain he'll give you all assistance possible."

"I'm most grateful, Colonel," Justine said.

"You'll never get there by the main road. It's jammed solid a few kilometers to the south." Vercours stepped to a wall map which he studied for a few moments. Then he traced a line with his forefinger. "There's another way into Dunkerque. The road is rough, but you'll make it. Anything is better than being caught in that mob on the coastal road. Let's find your drivers. I'll show them the route and order a few cases of rations loaded for you. At least the children won't have to go hungry again."

"Colonel Vercours, you're a fraud," Justine said. "A fraud busy playing the hard-boiled soldier, pretending to be tough when the opposite is true."

The colonel grinned. "You've discovered my weak spot—children. Back in Paris, I have three grandchildren, merciless little tyrants." He adjusted his cap and sighed. "I wonder if I'll ever see them again. Well, *c'est la guerre*. Shall we go?"

At that moment an anti-aircraft battery started banging away like a fist pounding on a wooden door. Sirens began wailing and alarm bells clanged.

"Air raid!" someone shouted.

Men rushed pell-mell for the woods. Black puffs of bursting anti-aircraft shells dotted the sky. Tracer bullets streaked upward as machine guns opened fire. Outside the hunting lodge Justine searched the sky but saw no planes. The colonel grabbed her by the arm. "Take cover in the woods," he commanded.

"I can't leave the children," she cried. Breaking away from him, she ran across the clearing toward the field kitchen where the group from *La Maison* had been gathered.

Just then, *Stukas* appeared directly overhead. Ignoring *flak* and tracer bullets, the planes went into steep dives, plastering the clearing with bombs. A random hit struck a fuel dump. Smoke and flames mushroomed from the gasoline drums. Chain-reaction explosions followed. The ground heaved and shook as though rocked by an earthquake.

Colonel Vercours sprinted after Justine as she vanished in the thick black smoke. Before he could reach her, the jagged splinters of an exploding bomb riddled his body and the colonel fell dead.

# 12

When the first bomb hit, Justine was thrown to the ground by the concussion. This saved her life. Bomb after bomb fell, but she pressed face downward against the buckling earth, hearing the bomb fragments zing through the air with a sound like swarms of maddened hornets.

She flinched at the noise, smoke and heat from the flaming gasoline drums. She dared not move in that hurricane of fury and death. She lay prostrate, fingers scrabbling in the dirt, awaiting the pain of metal piercing her body; she imagined herself ripped and bleeding, dead in that frightful carnage. She wept and begged for the bombing to end. She screamed until her throat was raw, but the ear-splitting explosions drowned her voice.

Then, it was all over.

The planes flew off, followed by the dirty gray blobs of anti-aircraft shells. A *Stuka* was hit. It wobbled crazily and then, trailing smoke and flames, went spinning to earth.

Justine did not move for a full minute after the raid ended. At last she lifted her head. A wall of

fire danced before her eyes. Bodies were lying in
the clearing. Bomb craters yawned all around. A
wounded man shrieked. Wildly she thought, I am
dead and this is Hell.

Soldiers appeared. Men with chemical fire extinguishers sprayed the flames; litter bearers came;
first-aid men dashed from body to body, looking for
wounded. A soldier with a Red Cross brassard
helped her get up.

"Are you hurt?" he asked, his young, beardless
face begrimed with dirt.

Justine shook her head, clinging to the soldier's
arm for support. She gasped, "My children—"

"Over there," the soldier said, pointing.

She staggered away from him and broke into a
lurching run. Stumbling, she plunged ahead. A man
loomed out of the smoke. He caught Justine as she
fell forward.

"It's me, Raoul," he said.

She clutched him. "Oh, thank God—the children?"

"They're all right. Shaken up, but not hurt. The
soldiers have a good shelter back there and took us
to it when the raid started."

"I was frantic. I thought—" Justine gulped hard.

"It was bad enough, but there we were snug and
safe, then everybody started worrying about you.
All the children were calling for *Tante Justine* and

making almost as much racket as the bombs. Come on, I'll bring you to them."

Nearby, soldiers with fire extinguishers were squirting chemical foam on two flaming trucks. Justine realized that the burning vehicles were those that had brought them from *La Maison*.

"Raoul, our trucks!" she cried. "What will we do?"

"We'll find other transportation. They're not the only trucks," Raoul said. He pointed with his cane. "This way, down the path into the woods."

They entered a glen where the shadows were deep and the war seemed in another world. Only the smoke swirling around the treetops gave any hint of the chaos outside. Raoul limped ahead to a jumble of boulders haphazardly deposited in that place millenniums earlier by some natural upheaval. The giant stones rested across a wide gully like a roof. An opening at the base of the rocks provided entry into the covered gully. It was as if fate had set those rocks down, tumbling them in this manner so that an accident of nature would give protection against man-made catastrophe.

As Raoul and Justine approached, children came running. Justine was hugged, mauled and kissed. Tiny laughing faces; skinny, wiry bodies; shrill, piercing voices, all talking at once; eager, loving arms; these were the children. Berthe clasped Justine in her arms. The cook's tears flowed. She sniffed and snuffled until her nose and eyes were red.

At last the enthusiastic welcome tapered off and the children surrounded Justine like puppies. A platoon of riflemen came tramping down the trail. The detachment was led by Sergeant Brunel, the military policeman who had guided the trucks to Fourth Division Headquarters. Brunel halted his men. "We're pulling out, madame. The whole division," he said glumly. "The engineers are booby-trapping and mining the area."

"I must see Colonel Vercours about transportation for us," Justine said.

"The colonel?" Brunel shook his head sadly. "Don't you know? He's dead. Killed in the air raid."

"The colonel—dead—" Justine repeated dully.

"He was a good soldier. We all respected him," Brunel said. "But he couldn't have done anything for you, there isn't a truck to spare in the division. We're marching to Dunkerque and you're welcome to join us."

"Sergeant, my children can't walk that far," Justine protested.

Brunel leaned on his rifle. "I'll put it to you straight, madame. The *boches* are in Ostend and they're coming this way fast. Walk or get captured. Dunkerque's only twenty or so kilometers from here, maybe a bit farther. You can do it. We'll see that you get there."

Justine clasped her hands tightly in a prayerful gesture. "You're sure there are no trucks, Sergeant?"

"I'm sure."

"Then we'll walk to Dunkerque!" Justine turned to the children. "You heard what we must do. Stay close together. No straggling. Obey orders. The older boys and girls keep an eye on the little ones. Is that understood?"

"Yes!" the children chorused.

They quickly formed a column of two's, the smallest up front, and Brunel deployed his men on the flanks. The march started at his signal, soldiers and children, side by side. Raoul hobbled along, falling farther back with each step. The hike went on and on with no letup. Sergeant Brunel set a fast pace. When a child faltered, a soldier carried him. Soon the youngest children were all riding piggy-back, clinging to the soldiers who trudged ahead, bowed under knapsacks, rifles, helmets and ammunition.

More troops followed, units of the Fourth Division, retreating to Dunkerque. All the while, *Stukas* crisscrossed the sky, bombing and strafing the main road. Anti-aircraft sent a barrage of *flak* up at the German planes, but failed to drive them off.

By late afternoon every step became a struggle of will power. Justine walked grimly, teeth gritted. She would forever remember this ordeal. The children, blurred by weariness, stumbled on like unstrung marionettes. Now and then, one would fall and be helped to his feet.

Once Berthe shrieked at Brunel. "Stop! Let us rest! Have you no mercy?"

The sergeant fixed her with a cold stare. "If you want mercy, fall out. Maybe you'll get mercy from the *boches*. We're going on!"

"Please don't leave me," Berthe cried.

"Then save your breath and keep walking," Brunel snapped.

So they went, through the woods, along a bumpy dirt road that led past charred farmhouses and blackened fields. To the east stretched sand dunes. Soon they would be passing Malo-les-Bains, with Dunkerque just beyond. The tang of the sea was in the air, but its freshness was tainted by smoke from burning towns, villages, homes and shops.

They staggered ahead, white dust masking strained faces. Far to the rear, Raoul, unable to go any farther, had dropped out. He picked up a rifle and a cartridge belt some soldier had thrown away. The road was littered with weapons, belts, knapsacks, extra clothing, tins of rations—the debris of a retreating army.

Taking the discarded rifle and the ammunition, Raoul found a good position among some rocks overlooking the road. Then the old man lit his pipe and awaited the Germans.

# Dunkerque

*"...on horror's head horrors accumulate..."*

# 1

During the march from Nieuport, Justine kept up her morale by clinging to the belief that once in Dunkerque her problems would be solved. The Belgian government officials there would provide food, clothing and shelter. Perhaps arrangements could be made to reunite the children with their parents. If this proved impossible, the officials might ship her to the south of France—somewhere on the Mediterranean coast. There she would establish a new *La Maison* for war orphans and refugee children.

They came to the outskirts of Dunkerque at sunset, but were to find no refuge. The city was in flames. Houses, buildings, docks made fiery beacons. Overhead roared flights of planes, incessantly dropping bombs on the burning ruins.

Dusty, weary soldiers trudged through the streets. Stragglers came, searching for their units. Deserters skulked in doorways and cellars as squads of military police combed the hiding places to ferret them out. Water shot up in twenty-foot-high geysers from broken mains. Sewage flooded the streets, spewing out of smashed pipes. Shattered glass tinkled down in a blizzard of crystal flakes.

This was the shambles Justine and her children reached at dusk, Saturday, May 18, 1940. They were aghast at the devastation; explosions sounded every few seconds. Walls collapsed, flames leaped skyhigh, people shouted and cursed; ambulances raced with screeching sirens; couriers on motorcycles rocketed by at perilous speeds. Dunkerque, which Justine had imagined to be an unshaken bastion, was instead vulnerable and mortally wounded.

Sergeant Brunel and his men had escorted the children to the city limits where a military police officer ordered the sergeant to round up deserters hiding in wrecked cottages on the beach. Justine and her little group stood forlornly against a wall and bid goodbye to Brunel and his men. Blinking hard, the sergeant shook hands with Justine.

"*Au revoir,* madame," he mumbled. "Good luck to you and the children."

"*Au revoir,* Sergeant," Justine said.

The men marched off, each turning for a farewell wave. Moments later Brunel's detachment vanished amid files of civilians and troops. Justine had never felt so lost, so alone. Raoul was missing. It seemed impossible to imagine going on without him. A sea of people trudged past, but these were heedless strangers, no one to whom she could reach out.

Mercier was gone. Marie was dead. She still had

Berthe but that good, devoted woman had broken on the march. The thin, wiry cook stood gray-faced, head bowed, trembling and cringing at every explosion. Justine saw that Berthe was in shock. She could no longer be counted on to take care of children, but rather needed looking after herself.

The center of Dunkerque lay about a kilometer from the spot where Justine was standing with her children. Somewhere in the vortex of that flame-swept wilderness were the men Justine wanted to find—the government officials who could help her. She stood undecided, reluctant to enter Dunkerque with her bevy of children. In her mind it would be leading them to certain death. But death was everywhere. They could not remain where they were. Bombs were falling like rain. The ground quivered under the blasts. In another few minutes the terrified children might break and run. Justine had to move quickly if she wanted to keep them together.

"We're going into Dunkerque," she cried above the racketing bombs. "Claude, Georges, Jacques and Louis. You will bring up the rear. Make sure nobody drops out," she ordered. "Now everyone take a partner and follow me." She led Berthe by the arm. The cook walked with her, unresisting, uncomprehending.

So they went, caught up in the human tide drifting toward Dunkerque. For many, the beleaguered city spelled the end of the road. The dead sprawled on sidewalks, in the slime-filled gutters; they lay huddled in hallways and shop entrances.

Wounded men, women and children limped along or sat propped against walls, quietly waiting to die. There were moans, shrieks of pain and piteous cries for water. Dunkerque had become a madhouse where dogs insane with fear ran yapping in the streets and fires raged unchecked.

Although badly hurt, the city fought back with the courage of a dying lion. Soldiers manned anti-aircraft guns set up around the docks. The rapid-firing cannon blasted away in pounding cadence. Searchlights swept the fire-tinged sky and *flak* bursts spattered like orange-hued mushrooms.

# 2

In Dunkerque Justine headed for the customs house where the town commandant, Admiral Platon, had his headquarters. Confused by guns, bombs, fires and noise, she lost her way. The children followed her down one street and up another. Timbers crashed, chimneys toppled and walls collapsed around them, but no one was hurt.

Justine tried to find a street leading to the customs house but every turning took her more deeply into a maze of winding dead-end alleys. She stumbled through a passageway which ran between a row of deserted stone houses so gutted by fire that only the walls stood.

The alley opened onto a cobblestone-paved square, blocked by an imposing wall and wrought-iron gates which hung ajar. A gilt-lettered sign arched above the gate. In the fading light Justine made out the words: *L'Ecole du Sacré Coeur*—the Sacred Heart School. She recalled that the school was situated in the old section of Dunkerque. Normally, a ten-minute walk would have brought her to the customs house. Now it seemed an interminable distance through a hellish inferno.

In contrast to the rest of Dunkerque, no bombs were falling near the school; no fires burned. Only a few blocks away explosions thundered incessantly. The very ground heaved and trembled. Tremendous pillars of fire leaped skyward. But *L'Ecole du Sacré Coeur* stood tranquilly in its quaint Old World square, undamaged and undisturbed.

Justine could see no signs of life in the school building, a massive gray stone edifice with a domed roof. She pushed the gates open and climbed the time-worn steps to the great oaken door. A pull bell-cord dangled over the entrance. She yanked it hard. A bell clanged deep in the interior of the building and frantically she pulled on the cord again and again. The bell resounded hollowly inside.

Just as she was losing hope that anyone would open the door, the portal swung open. An old, bearded man in a priest's cassock, carrying a kerosene lantern, stood in the entrance. He held the lamp high so that its beam shone on Justine and the children clustered behind her.

"What is it? Who are you?" the priest asked.

"Father, please let us in," Justine pleaded.

The cleric stepped aside and beckoned them to enter. When all were in, he set down the lantern, closed the door and slid the heavy crossbar in place to lock it. By the lantern's light, Justine made out a wide staircase that led to the upper floors and a long corridor which disappeared into the darkness at the rear of the building.

Justine quickly told their story to Father Gorot, the priest. When she had finished, he shook his head sadly.

"These are terrible days," he said. "Terrible days. To think innocent children should be victims." He paused and drew a deep breath. "I'm alone here. The others left after the first bombings—teachers, priests, students. But I stayed. I'm too old to run, especially from the *boches*."

"You're the only one here?" Justine asked. "How do you manage?"

"The cellar is stocked with edibles. I was about to go out and tell the authorities, but now that you are here—" He looked at her and smiled. "Would you be my guests? I'd like company."

Before she could answer, they heard the screech of falling bombs. "Down!" Father Gorot shouted. "They're coming straight at us."

With amazing speed, the aged priest dropped prone. Everyone went to the floor. Justine pulled Berthe with her, just as the bombs exploded in the square directly outside. The impact of the blast ripped the doors off their hinges and shook the building. Windowpanes shattered. The acrid smell of cordite filled the air. For a few moments after the explosion, no one stirred. A stunned death-like silence hung like a curtain. A child whimpered. Another moved and sat up, looking wide-eyed at the great doors hanging askew and splintered by shrapnel fragments.

Berthe scrambled to her feet, eyes bulging in terror. She waved her arms wildly, threw back her head and let out an unearthly scream. Then, babbling incoherently, legs flailing like an animated scarecrow's, she dashed for the wrecked doorway and started clambering past the sagging doors.

Justine rose from the floor. "Berthe! Berthe! Come back!" she cried, rushing after the frenzied cook.

The boy Georges, followed by Jacques, Claude and Louis, scrambled toward Berthe, as the other children looked on fearfully. Father Gorot also ran to the entrance. With the boys close behind her, Justine reached Berthe first. She grabbed the cook and tried to pull her back. But Berthe, with insane strength, thrust Justine aside. Knobby fists flying, she beat off the four boys and flung herself into the street.

She fled through the darkness, wild shrieks trailing behind. Before Justine or anyone else could chase her, more bombs bracketed the square. Berthe was blown almost fifteen feet into the air and crashed to the cobblestones with bone-smashing force. The explosions were still echoing and shrapnel clattering on the pavement as Justine and the boys dashed across the square to Berthe. A glance told Justine that her long-time friend was dead. The four boys ran up and stopped in their tracks, breathing hard, as Justine dropped to her knees and wept.

Father Gorot came and gestured the boys to leave. "Look after the little ones," he told them, "they need you." Glancing down at Berthe, he genuflected, made the sign of the cross and prayed. Justine remained kneeling, her cheeks wet with tears.

The priest finished his prayer. He took Justine's arm and drew her erect. "Come, my daughter. We can do no good here," he said, leading her back inside the school.

Justine moved like a sleepwalker. She was in a state of shock, stunned by the sudden tragedy. She clamped shut her eyes, trying to erase the awful memory of Berthe twisting through the air but it was etched in her brain. For all the days of her life she would see that sight over and over again.

She shuddered and gave a little moan, turning her back on the white-faced children to hide her tears. She wept bitterly until Father Gorot placed his hand on her shoulder.

"Dry your eyes," he said gently. "Do not use up your strength in mourning. You have to think of these young lives, a God-given task that has fallen on your shoulders."

Justine nodded and lifted her grief-stricken face. "Father, Father, tell me what to do. I'm so terribly frightened," she whispered.

The priest smiled tenderly. "Of course you're frightened. But take comfort in the words of Our Saviour: 'Be of good cheer; it is I; be not afraid.' In His wisdom, He knew fear was part of man. Yet we must rise above it and gain strength from our faith in Him."

"Yes, Father." Justine swallowed hard. She wiped away the tears with the back of a grimy hand. She looked at her dirt-crusted fingers and smiled wanly. "I haven't had a wash for a week. I must look a sight."

A string of explosions rattled the broken windows. Glass shards tinkled to the floor.

"It's no longer safe up here. Follow me to the cellar," Father Gorot said.

They trooped behind the priest who led them down the long corridor, lighting the way with the kerosene lamp. At the end of the hallway, he pulled open a creaking, ponderous wooden door. A flight of steps dropped steeply into a huge cellar.

"Mind the stairs. Keep close to the wall and go slowly. It's a big drop," Father Gorot called as he started down.

The cautious descent seemed endless. The single lantern, with its feeble beam, barely pierced the blackness of the vast basement. Justine moved a step at a time, pressing against the rough stone wall, feeling its dampness under her hands. Behind her she heard the children sobbing and understood their terror. If the darkness pressed on her with the weight of a thousand fears, how it must be magnified in a child's mind. She fought down a sense of panic fed by the tomblike dankness rising from the depths below. A stumble on these time-eroded stone steps could mean injury or death.

Swallowing her own feelings, Justine paused and said lightly, "We've been through worse than this, *mes enfants.* Down we go, one step at a time. And soon we'll be at the bottom, safe and sound. Slowly, carefully. One step at a time."

The children obeyed her. They came down in single file without mishap. By then Father Gorot had lit a number of candles. Their cheery glow dispelled many of the imaginary terrors that had been lurking in the black recesses. The cellar was enormous, a medieval dungeon with vaulted ceilings and thick stone walls. Moisture hung in beady drops from ceiling and walls. Somewhere, off in the unlit portion, water was dripping. Dampness rose out of the stone floor; the air was musty, like that in a long-closed mausoleum.

Passageways led off the main cellar like tunnels in a mine. Every sound raised hollow echoes. The children huddled glumly around Justine, pressing against her for comfort. She could give them none; mute misery overwhelmed her. She shivered, but could not tell whether from the cellar chill or sudden dread.

So they stood, a dejected, downhearted group. Above, they heard the dull booming of the bombs.

And suddenly Georges piped up in his reedy twelve-year-old voice, "*Tante Justine,* we shouldn't be so gloomy. It's a lot better than being out there. With all those bombs going off, someone could get hurt." Georges faltered. "I mean— I mean— Oh, you know what I mean."

"Yes, Georges, I do," Justine said. "We're all feeling so sorry for ourselves that we don't appreciate being safe and sound."

"Yes! Yes!" Georges cried eagerly, "That's what I was trying to say. Things could be worse!"

" 'Out of the mouths of babes,' " Father Gorot quoted. "Let's be of good cheer. I think we'll all feel better after something to eat. Are you hungry, children?"

A great shout went up. The priest smoothed his beard. "Well, let me see what can be done about that."

He picked up his lantern and strode down one of the mysterious passageways, his footfalls echoing back. Soon he returned, arms laden with smoked sausages and round red Edam cheeses.

"It's no royal feast. But this is about the best the storage room had to offer," he said.

The priest produced a knife and for the next few minutes was busy cutting generous chunks of sausage and big slices of cheese, which were handed out to the children.

Father Gorot thoughtfully chewed a piece of sausage as he spoke to Justine. "You'll be all right here for tonight, but this damp cellar is no place for the children. They'll all be sick in no time at all."

"I know that, Father. I want to get them out of here, out of Dunkerque. I must find Admiral Platon, he'll have contact with my government's people," Justine said.

"You won't reach him tonight. The *boches* are busier than usual. As a rule, they don't hit us as hard in the daylight when the anti-aircraft guns have a better shot at them. Spend the night here, and in the morning you can see the admiral. Leave the children with me when you go. I'll look after them until your return," Father Gorot suggested.

"Yes, Father. Thank you," Justine said.

So they had been granted some respite for a few hours; a brief stay of execution. She was grateful for that much. The war had exacted a bitter price already. Marcel missing. Marie and Berthe killed. Mercier and Raoul missing. Colonel Vercours killed. How much higher would the toll rise? Fortunately, the casualty list did not yet include any of the children. But could they go on facing bombs, shells and bullets without suffering losses? That was in the hands of God. Until now, He had protected them. She could only pray that He would continue to do so.

# 3

Sunday, May 19, 1940 was a Sabbath marked by violence previously unequaled in history. Guns snarled and men died. Bombs dropped and cities turned to rubble. Never had the insanity of war been so apparent. But hate had clouded men's minds and all reason was gone. It was a war to the death; naked and brutal, without mercy or restraint.

At daybreak, silence hung over Dunkerque. A fitful, brooding silence as yet unbroken by the crash of bombs, the hammering of anti-aircraft cannon, the stutter of machine guns, or the screams of the dying.

Dunkerque was like a painting by a mad artist. Fires still burned and wreckage blocked the streets. Dogs sniffed at bloated corpses. It was a city of desolation, death and despair. But its stubborn defense continued. Increasing daylight revealed soldiers marching to posts in different parts of the city. During the night, retreating units had reached Dunkerque, bringing with them dozens of anti-aircraft guns and field artillery pieces.

The new *flak* batteries took up positions along the battered waterfront to protect the docks. The field-pieces were placed to sweep the city's approaches. As they drew closer to Dunkerque, the Nazis would come against increased resistance; thousands of Allied troops were being forced back upon the city and meant to fight the enemy down to the last cartridge.

With the end of night, refugees emerged, like ghosts, from hiding places. Once again they formed a melancholy procession plodding the road to nowhere. After more than a week most civilians were on foot; cars had long ago been wrecked, destroyed or abandoned for lack of fuel. Now the exodus was slower, more labored.

Strain showed on people's faces. Everyone seemed old, with bent frame and lackluster eyes. The ashen mass hobbled onward. Even children looked wizened and pinched. No voice was raised in song or laughter and among all those thousands, no one smiled.

On the waterfront the burned-out hulks of several bombed freighters lurched at their moorings. Although the piers had been damaged and wharfside facilities leveled, the *Luftwaffe* had failed to paralyze the port.

Several merchantmen were tied up, taking on wounded soldiers, mostly British, bound for England. Walking wounded, with blood-soaked bandages, went painfully up gangplanks. Torn, mutilated men were carried aboard on stretchers. The embarkations were made in silence except for shuffling feet, muted orders and groans.

The ship's crews looked aloft anxiously, praying the *Stukas* would not catch them helplessly moored. Out in the Channel a vessel had a chance to evade the bombs and the strafing; but here, at anchor, ships made easy targets.

It was small comfort to see numerous anti-aircraft batteries ranged along the dock area, slender barrels pointing up like so many accusing fingers. Everyone knew the guns could neither destroy nor drive off all the planes. In a mass raid, some aircraft always got through, no matter how intensive the curtain of *flak*.

Fighter planes were needed to deal with the enemy, but the only available fighters—R.A.F. *Spitfires* and *Hurricanes*—were based across the Channel on English soil. The British airmen flew several protective sorties a day over Dunkerque, knocked down a few German planes and headed home, leaving the sky to the *Luftwaffe*.

Out beyond the breakwater which formed Dunkerque's natural harbor, sleek-hulled British and French warships patroled the waters; slim destroyers prowled, relentlessly hunting for U-boats, while cruisers guarded against an attack by Nazi warships.

The *Stukas* had hurled themselves against the warships only to meet disaster. Rapid-firing navy anti-aircraft pompoms blasted the dive bombers in mid-air. The much-feared Nazi plane was effective against land targets or anchored ships, but could not cope with hard-hitting destroyers and cruisers. Although sorely pressed, the Allies struck back in sharp defense. The German radio boasted daily that all enemy resistance had been "eliminated." Gloating announcers described to credulous listeners how Dunkerque, Calais and Boulogne had fallen. Victory-flushed civilians danced in the streets of Berlin, Munich, Hamburg and other large cities. Crowds paraded outside Nazi headquarters in Berlin to serenade the *Fuehrer* and when Hitler appeared on the balcony, the masses roared, *"Sieg Heil!"* until windows rattled for blocks around.

But this noisy jubilation did not alter the fact that the *Wehrmacht* still had a lot of fighting to do before the fantasies of home-front propagandists became realities. On the Allied side, no one, including Admiral Platon, the commandant of Dunkerque, doubted that the Nazis eventually would take the city. Platon's job was to delay the inevitable as long as possible. He had been ordered to gain time, not to win a victory.

Admiral Platon, a crusty seadog, was a cool-headed, efficient officer. He ran Dunkerque firmly, seeing to its defense, making certain that ships moved freely in the port and preventing chaos by keeping the torrent of refugees moving out of the city toward Calais and Boulogne.

He was afraid the homeless thousands would swamp Dunkerque and hinder proper military movement. The rugged sailor gave a sigh of relief when officials of the Belgian government evacuated Dunkerque during the afternoon of Saturday, May 18. He had no use for politicians of any nationality and resented the added burden of looking after cabinet members, deputies and senators.

Unceasing bombardment by the *Luftwaffe* had convinced the august Belgian officials that Dunkerque was no place for them. Staying only one day, they left in a long motor convoy; the last Admiral Platon had heard, the dignitaries were in Boulogne, debating whether to take ship for England.

Hapless civilian refugees pouring into Dunkerque jammed the piers trying to get aboard any craft capable of crossing the Channel. At first Platon permitted some to take the Dunkerque-Dover ferry, which plied its run despite the bombs. The sturdy Channel steamers made the journey loaded to the gunwales with passengers. On several trips so many persons packed aboard that the decks were awash. Terrible disorders broke out on the docks as anxious refugees pressed around the ferry-line ticket windows.

Men fought, women were knocked down and children trampled. The ticket sellers were offered huge bribes; money, jewelry, watches, diamond rings were thrust at them in return for a ticket. The pasteboard slip had more value than the most precious gems.

The admiral soon realized he could not continue to allow unrestricted travel on the ferries. The dangers of a full-scale riot were great. The possibility that an overloaded ferryboat might capsize was always present. Platon prohibited any further departures by sea from Dunkerque except by authorized military personnel, sick or wounded soldiers, and injured civilians. The rest had to find their own escape.

"I'm neither cruel nor barbarous," the admiral declared, as protests mounted against his order. "No able-bodied person, military or civilian, will board ship here while I'm in command. The space on those vessels is reserved for those unable to help themselves. As for the others, unfortunately, it is a situation of *sauve qui peut*—every man for himself."

Troops with fixed bayonets cleared a two-block area around the docks. Barbed wire barricades were erected and the guards had orders to shoot to kill if necessary. A few desperate civilians tried to climb the barrier, only to be shot down. This restored a semblance of order on the docks. Control points manned by military police gave access to the loading piers and allowed fairly systematic boarding of vessels. Despite eight days of unrelenting bombings, sea traffic remained brisk between Dunkerque and England.

At some piers, stevedores worked frantically to

empty vessels still carrying peacetime goods. One such merchantman, a 9,000-ton freighter, the *Adeleine,* flying the French flag, had a cargo of jute aboard. A huge power crane used for unloading was disabled by a bomb hit and a crew of stevedores toiled to haul the jute ashore by hand. That highly inflammable material still rested in the ship's hold after a week. The longshoremen could not work during bombings and, as a result of the frequent air-raid alarms, had only succeeded in emptying slightly more than half the ship's hold.

The stevedores were swarming over the *Adeleine* at daybreak. Platon wanted her ready by nightfall; she could carry several hundred wounded to hospitals in England. Now work gangs sweated under huge bales of jute, staggering up the companionways and out to the pier, always with an eye cocked for German planes.

On such a morning, in such an atmosphere, Justine Raymond awoke after an uncomfortable night in the school cellar. The children were restless. A few had developed hacking coughs from the penetrating dampness. Several were feverish. Another night in this place might bring on an outbreak of grippe or pneumonia. She had to get them out of there.

Father Gorot tried to cheer the group. He cupped a hand around one ear and listened with mock intensity. "I don't hear any bombs. Maybe the war's over. We'd like that, wouldn't we, children?" His sally brought no response. The children stood in silence. Someone coughed raspingly. Taken aback, Father Gorot covered his confusion by rubbing his hands together briskly. "How about some breakfast, eh? We'll all feel better with full bellies. I'll see what I can find back there in the storeroom," he said heartily.

Justine stopped him with a gesture. "Wait, Father. I'm going to see Admiral Platon. You'll look after the children?"

"Madame Raymond, I gave my promise. They'll be safe with me, I assure you. But do take something to eat first."

"No, thanks, I'm not hungry. I'd better have a word with the children." She stepped away from the priest and clapped her hands for attention. "*Mes enfants*, I must leave for a little while. Father Gorot will be with you. I'll be back soon, with good news."

A frightened wail arose from the children, an animal cry of fear. "Don't go away, *Tante Justine!*" a small girl begged.

"Yvette, Yvette, my little one. I'll be back very soon." Justine embraced the child, stroking her tangled blonde hair. "I'm going for help, that's all. Don't be afraid, sweetheart. I'll be here before you know it."

Yvette shook her head vigorously and squirmed away. "No! You'll be dead, like Marie and Berthe," she screamed, and ran sobbing to the wall.

The other children looked on numbly, turning from Yvette to Justine and back again. Justine was torn between remaining to comfort the weeping girl and leaving. After a momentary hesitation, she made up her mind. This was a time for firmness, not emotion.

"Listen, all of you," she said sharply. "I think you'll understand. We can't stay here! I must see the authorities."

"Take us with you!" a boy cried.

"No! I can't go around these streets with fifty children. You've been brave up to now. Hang on a little longer. I promise I'll be back." She swung abruptly to face Father Gorot. "I'm leaving now, Father."

"Do you know the way to the customs house?" the priest asked.

"I'll find it," she said.

"I would go in your place, madame, but I—I'm too old. I can't walk that far," Father Gorot apologized. "I'm sorry."

"Father, give me your blessing," Justine asked.

The priest bowed his head in prayer. He made the sign of the cross over her. She genuflected and crossed herself, then walked to the long stone staircase and began to climb up.

# 4

Justine picked her way through rubble that blocked the streets. Dunkerque was ugly in the May sunshine. Darkness had cloaked the scars left by the bombers. Now she saw the ruin. The bombs had played terrible pranks. In one street a home was left standing, its front wall blown off. As in a doll's house, the rooms were exposed, showing furniture neatly in place, beds made, the dining-room table still set for a dinner never eaten.

Sunlight made rainbows in the spray of water spouting from mains. Glass crunched under her feet. An overturned baby carriage, splattered with blood, blocked her way and she walked around it, stabbed by a pang of grief for the infant who had died there. The horrors of war confronted her everywhere: a dead man crumpled in a roadway; two school-age girls lying side by side in the front garden of a burned-out house. Death reached out of every corner.

Yet the living still went on. She passed a squad of young soldiers gathered around a small cooking fire in the shattered remains of a building. They were drinking coffee from tin mess cups, joking and laughing.

As she neared the center of town, Justine was caught up in a mass of civilians stumbling apathetically along. She elbowed through the unheeding throng; no one spoke, no one paused. The refugees had long ceased to think or feel. Numbed and dazed, they had only enough will left to keep up the search for safety.

St. Eloi's damaged spire gleamed in the sun. In the *Place Jean Bart,* the hero stood on his pedestal, undaunted. The statue's base had been chipped by flying shrapnel and gaping holes yawned in the pavement, but Jean Bart remained unscathed, sternly gazing out to sea, his jaw set in timeless defiance of the enemy.

A few blocks from the *Place Jean Bart* ran a tree-lined avenue leading to the customs house. The tall, graceful trees were broken and uprooted. The once beautiful street was a shambles; puddles of stagnant water in the roadway formed small lakes. The shops and cafés that once marked the street were fire-gutted. Chairs, tables, furniture, clothing, books scattered by bomb blasts had been hurled helter-skelter. The smashed glass of shop windows twinkled merrily in the sunlight.

The massive gray stone customs house with its imposing façade and green-hued copper dome had been built at the foot of the avenue many years before. The customs house had baroque decoration, intricate stone carvings and ornate iron work. It was a well-known Dunkerque landmark. The motto of France, *Liberté, Egalité et Fraternité,* was emblazoned above the main entrance in carved letters two feet high. Gargoyles leered down on the street below and over all flew the tricolor from its tall flagstaff atop the dome.

The venerable building bore the marks of battle. Bombs had damaged its dome. The front and sides of the customs house were slashed by shrapnel fragments. Sandbagged machine-gun positions dotted the flat rooftops of the structure's wings. The French flag still fluttered from its pole, but the banner was frayed and ripped by German metal. Heavily armed sentries paced at the entrance doors.

Nearby were the docks. Through a skeleton framework of burned docksheds the crews unloading the *Adeleine* were visible. From his office on the second floor of the customs house, Admiral Henri Platon saw how slowly the work was progressing.

Platon was exasperated. He had expected the ship to be ready by daybreak. It was now 6:30 A.M. and the stevedores still had not emptied the forward hatch. The commandant picked up a telephone and shouted into it. By God, he had wanted the *Adeleine* to sail on the morning tide. There were more than five hundred wounded men lying like dogs on stretchers awaiting transport to England aboard her.

Despite Platon's ire, the dock supervisor told him the *Adeleine* could not sail until 3 P.M. The admiral slammed down the receiver and cursed.

But he did not have much time to indulge his anger. Couriers scurried back and forth with despatches. Telephones jangled. Officers stomped in and out. Reports flashed over the radio. A flight of fifty *Stukas* heading for Dunkerque from the west. A convoy strafed by *Luftwaffe* planes on the Calais road. A German *panzer* attack smashed by British units to the east. Place names of the First World War crackled over the radio: Mons, Tournai, Panne, Adinkerke, Ypres, Hazebrouck, Armentières. Everywhere, the Germans. Everywhere, fighting. The ring closing in. Tighter and tighter. The *panzers* were at Cambrai where in 1916 the British had first used tanks. The Nazis had taken Lille and Le Cateau, scenes of drawn-out sanguine battles in 1914–18.

They had overrun Verdun, that hallowed field made fertile by the blood of more than 300,000 Frenchmen in the other war. Verdun, where the embattled *poilus* had gone to their deaths shouting the rallying cry *"Ils ne passeront pas!"*—"They Shall Not Pass!"—a slogan that had electrified France and the world. Now, the *boches* had Verdun and the glory of another time was tarnished.

Platon rose from his littered desk. He walked to a window and stared down into the street. What a disaster! One could barely recognize Dunkerque. Ah, the *boches,* the diabolical *boches.* War was in their blood.

The telephone rang. A spot of good news. R.A.F. fighters had broken up the *Stuka* formation coming to Dunkerque. Six enemy planes downed and the flight scattered. Little reason to cheer. The *Luftwaffe* would be around again, Platon mused. Absently, he smoothed his mustache with a forefinger. The ring was closing. Tighter. Tighter.

Justine was about a block from the customs house when the air-raid sirens sounded at 6:45 A.M. She broke into a run as everyone on the street scattered. A motorcycle despatch rider turned on full throttle and spun around a corner at a perilous angle. Soldiers sprinted past, leaping for cover in bombed-out houses. The sirens wailed like souls in torment. Anti-aircraft guns searched the sky for the raiders. All at once, the destroyers out beyond the harbor mouth loosed a barrage from their rapid-firing pompoms. The flat explosions drifted into the city like distant applause. Shell bursts stippled the sky above the warships.

Justine stopped and shading her eyes from the sun, spotted the silvery glint of *Stukas* trying to evade the anti-aircraft fire. One plane burst into flames, then another, The surviving *Stukas* fled in a northerly direction. Dunkerque was temporarily free of German planes.

The sirens sounded "All Clear" and traffic resumed. Soldiers ducked out of the shelters. Refugees reappeared in the streets. Military vehicles rolled again. Workers on the *Adeleine* resumed operations.

Walking briskly, Justine soon arrived at the customs house. She started up the steps but a sentry barred her way. He was a wide-shouldered man with a dark stubble of beard. Holding his bayoneted rifle at port, he growled: "What do you want, madame?"

"I'd like to see Admiral Platon," Justine said.

"You have a pass? Nobody goes in without a pass," the sentry rasped.

"I don't have a pass. But I must see the admiral," Justine insisted.

"Go on, get out of here," the sentry ordered. He nudged her with the rifle butt.

Quick, hot anger flashed through Justine. She saw the hard, unshaven face of the sentry frozen into a cruel mask. After all she had suffered, to be turned away like this was too much. Hardly aware of what she was doing, Justine leaped at the soldier, clawing, kicking and screaming.

"Brute! Assassin!" she shouted. "You can't stop me! I *will* see the admiral! I will!"

The surprised sentry backed away under her furious assault. He tried to fend off her blows and kicks, at the same time yelling, "Corporal of the guard! Corporal of the guard! Post one!"

A few soldiers came on the run and the scuffle on the steps drew a crowd. Soldiers, civilians, sailors,

longshoremen gathered to watch. A corporal grabbed
Justine, who struggled even harder and screamed
still louder.

"Admiral Platon! Admiral Platon!" she shouted.

"Let her alone!" an onlooker bawled and charged
forward.

He was followed by a yelling crowd. A free-for-all
exploded in a few furious seconds. Strangers swung
at each other; men rolled on the ground, grunting,
cursing, punching. Soldiers and sailors battled it out.
Taut nerves snapped, tensions spilled over into violence. The days and nights of terror and grief boiled
into fury. A full-scale riot was underway when squads
of club-swinging military police rushed in to quell
the disorder. A lively, noisy melee broke out. At the
height of the fighting, Admiral Platon, surrounded
by several staff officers, appeared in the doorway.

After some turbulent minutes, the tumult subsided. Rioters with cracked heads staggered off.
Scores had bloody noses, blackened eyes, puffed lips.
But their rage had burned out and bottled-up frus-
trations were spent.

The corporal who had seized Justine somehow had
managed to hang on to her during the fracas. When
the outbreak ended, Admiral Platon roared in a
terrible voice, "What the devil started this?"

The sentry who had been on duty pointed at Justine. "She's the one! She set it off!" He spoke with
some difficulty through swollen lips.

Platon turned a gelid stare on Justine. "Well, madame, what have you to say?"

"Admiral Platon, your friend Colonel Vercours said you would help me."

Platon stared at Justine. He bowed his head for an instant and then looked up. "Release her, Corporal. Come with me, madame."

Justine followed Platon to his office. He closed the door to shut out the clamoring noise of the headquarters. "Now, then, madame—?" he said, looking at her inquiringly, "I don't know your name."

"Raymond. Justine Raymond. . . ."

"Madame Raymond, I see by your uniform that you're a nurse. Were you with Pierre—Colonel Vercours—at the end?"

"I was near him. He was killed in an air raid on his command post near Nieuport."

"An air raid," Platon repeated. He took a deep breath and regained his composure. "Madame Raymond, will you please tell me what the fuss outside was about?"

"I wanted to see you and the sentry tried to stop me."

"As he was ordered to do."

"I had to see you."

"Why?"

Justine told her story briefly. When she finished the recital, Platon shook his head in wonder. "You kept fifty children together all the way from Heyst?

A remarkable feat. You deserve much credit, madame. I salute you."

"I couldn't have done it alone. I had good friends, and I lost them." She compressed her lips and fought back the tears.

"We've all lost a lot," the admiral said in a comforting tone. "How can I help you?"

"I was told Belgian government officials were here. Do you know where I can find them?"

"They're gone. Left yesterday. Last I heard they were at Boulogne. Must be in England by now."

"Oh, no! I was counting on them," Justine exclaimed, dismayed.

"What did you think they would do?"

"I'm not sure; perhaps get the children to their parents or evacuate us to Southern France. After all, they're the authorities, the government. Oh, I'm so confused."

Platon went to the window and crooked a finger at Justine. "See that ship out there?" he asked, pointing to the *Adeleine*.

"Yes, sir."

"She's sailing to England this afternoon, carrying wounded. Would you like to be aboard with your children?"

"To England!"

"It's the only way. You can't travel any farther south. This is the last stop, madame. Even now the engineers are blowing the bridges between Calais and Boulogne. According to my reports, the *boches* will take those ports soon. But we can and will defend Dunkerque to the end. I'll send a truck for your children and you can be out of this hell before sunset. What do you say?"

Justine frowned in thought. Should she take the children to England, away from homeland, parents, friends? How would they live in a foreign country, not even speaking the language, thrown among strangers? She had no money, no proper clothing for the children, nothing but what they had on their backs.

She thought of them huddled in the cellar of *L'Ecole du Sacré Coeur* with no one to care for them but a very old man. She thought of all they had endured. How could young minds stand the horrors of that ordeal? Uprooted, disinherited by the Nazi scourge, these tender children had suffered a lifetime of agony. She had to take them out of it, away from the war.

She looked at the *Adeleine* for a long time. At last in a strained voice she said, "We'll go to England."

"Good! The youngsters will be better off out of here. Get them ready. I'll have a man drive you back to *L'Ecole*. Do you mind riding in a motorcycle sidecar?" Admiral Platon asked.

"I never rode in one."

"There's always a first time for everything." He picked up a phone and spoke briefly. In a few seconds there was a knock on the door.

"*Entrez!*" Platon commanded.

A soldier wearing a leather helmet and goggles entered, saluted smartly and stood at attention. "Drive Madame Raymond to *L'Ecole du Sacré Coeur*. Do you know the place?"

"Yes, sir," the soldier said.

"Good. Madame, I'll make the necessary arrangements. I wish you *bon voyage*." Platon extended his hand, and shook hers warmly.

"Thank you, Admiral. Colonel Vercours was right. He said you were a good man."

"We were friends for many years. I'll miss him." Platon went to his desk and reached for the telephone. Justine followed the soldier out of the office.

The driver helped her into the sidecar of a motorcycle and mounted his seat. The machine started with a great roar. At that precise moment the sirens sounded an air raid. Anti-aircraft guns began to shoot. The soldier shouted, "Hold on tight! I'll run for it!"

The machine bounced wildly on the bumpy road. Bombs began to fall. Justine crouched low, listening to the ponderous *whump, whump* of the missiles. Overhead she heard many airplane motors. The *Luftwaffe* had come back with a vengeance.

As the motorcycle drew abreast of the dock where the *Adeleine* was moored, a tremendous explosion shook the area. Justine had one quick glimpse of the ship, enveloped in flames, heaving out of the water.

*The Long Escape*

The bomb blast overturned the speeding motorcycle. Justine felt herself hurtling through the air and only had time enough to think, my God, this is the end! Oh, the poor children!

And then came darkness.

# 5

First there was dull pain hammering at the base of her skull, then an awareness of noise—motors, guns, explosions. Finally, Justine opened her eyes, and stared up at the blue sky where fleecy white clouds drifted lazily in the freshening breeze. She saw the puffballs of *flak,* like muddy splotches against the clean blanket of the sky.

She forced herself to sit up. A wave of dizziness overwhelmed her and then passed. Justine looked around her; the motorcycle was lying on its side about ten yards away. A little closer, she saw the driver, his head twisted at a grotesque angle. She could tell his neck was broken. The *Adeleine* was burning furiously, tremendous sheets of fire leaping from her hull.

She saw that only a lucky fall had saved her life. A grassy shoulder fringed the dock road. When the motorcycle overturned, she had been catapulted onto the grass which cushioned the impact. She got to her feet with difficulty. The air raid was not yet over, but the action had moved to another part of the city. Anti-aircraft guns barked and *Stukas* came swooping out of the sun, their engines snarling like vicious dogs locked in a death struggle.

Justine did not know how long she had been unconscious. The heat and sparks from the flames consuming the *Adeleine* had caused the fire to spread. Vehicles parked near the dock were ablaze. The jute on the pier caught fire with a wooshing sound. Smaller fires joined until a great wall of flame enfolded the dock.

Justine limped away, heading in the direction of the school. She had to rejoin the children; only this made her keep going. The air raid had created fresh havoc. The smoke of a dozen fires swirled through the streets to form a choking haze so thick that it blocked out the sun in some places.

She went on, climbing over smoldering rubble, to make her slow way. All about Justine saw shadowy figures dashing through the smoke. Dream shapes that emerged and disappeared in the veil. She ached all over; her body was bruised; the throbbing in her head grew more violent. Once she fell and lay face down in the cinders and ashes of a dead fire. It seemed impossible to rise and continue her nightmare walk; staying there to die was easier, she thought.

The last chance for escape, the *Adeleine,* was a burning hulk. She had tried and failed. Dunkerque was to be her tomb and the children's. But something drove her to get up again. She could not say whether hatred, fear or love goaded her on. She reeled and staggered through destroyed streets, never certain where she was, for the familiar landmarks had been altered or destroyed in the bombing. She was a wanderer in an alien land, without guidepost or beacon.

Down one street, up another she went. Her hair hung in wild disarray. A burn welt ridged one cheek and lacerations crisscrossed the backs of her hands. The once starched nurse's uniform hung crumpled and soot-stained; she had not been out of her clothes in more than a week. Her face was smudged and blackened. Tears streamed from her smarting eyes. Stumbling, falling, rising, Justine forced her outraged legs to keep moving.

She paused for breath in a deserted square, clinging to a sagging gatepost for support. She seemed alone in a world devoid of life. The sun shone sickly yellow through the shifting smoke. This was a wilderness, a shadow place ruled by death. She clung to the gatepost until some of her waning strength returned. Somewhere bombs thudded and the guns slammed in persistent rhythms.

A sudden breeze cleared the smoke temporarily and even in the welter of ruin, Justine saw that she was only a short distance from *L'Ecole du Sacré Coeur.* Only a little longer and she would be back with the children. What could she tell them? *Mes enfants,* the rescue ship is at the bottom of the harbor and all our hopes are drowned with it. She would have to see them sicken and die before her eyes, helpless to save them.

Or perhaps it was already too late. The German bombers might have ended the children's terror and anxieties. She would come to the school to find that old building a jumbled heap of fallen masonry with red tongues of fire licking the formless ruin. Her thoughts whirled and in panic she began to run.

Four soldiers rounded a corner, walking with bowed heads, sagging shoulders and shuffling steps. Their slung rifles were canted at odd angles. They wore the uniform of Belgian Reserve Infantry. Justine stopped in her tracks, staring in disbelief at the approaching men. One was stout and she could see the sun glinting on his eyeglasses. Her heart pounded rapidly as she stood rooted, staring at the soldiers.

The stout man glanced up and she saw his face.

"Marcel!" she cried, lurching toward him.

The soldier stopped and squinted at her in bewilderment.

"Justine! In God's name, Justine!" he exclaimed. "It's my wife, men! My wife!"

Justine pushed past the three riflemen and rushed into Marcel's arms. One of his companions said gruffly, "We'll be down the street, Marcel."

"Can you beat it? He meets his wife here. There's one for the record!" a second soldier grinned. *"C'est la guerre!"*

Marcel and Justine swayed in wordless embrace. At last they parted. His face was tense and drawn, the face of a soldier who had seen much fighting.

"Where have you been, Marcel?" she asked.

"To Hell and back," he said. "We fought them every step, Justine, but it was impossible. You can't fight tanks with your bare hands. And the *Stukas*—every day, all day." He gestured toward his friends. "We four are the only ones left of our company. The rest of the battalion's supposed to be here, in Dunkerque. But you, Justine, what happened? How do you come here?"

She briefly described the events which had led her to Dunkerque. Marcel looked at her tenderly.

"We never even dreamed of such bitter days. Do you remember our last visit to Dunkerque, Justine?"

"Yes. Dunkerque in the summertime." She sighed, choked with sadness. "Soon it will be summer again."

"Oh, Justine, the world's gone crazy. I can't believe that Marie and Berthe are dead. Raoul gone. The children driven like sheep. Everything lost, smashed, everything."

Justine gripped his arm. "Marcel, let's get away, just the two of us. We'll find some escape, maybe get killed, but at least we shall die together."

"Hush. That's nonsense. We can't throw off our responsibilities," Marcel said. "I must find my battalion and fight on to the last. Each of us has a duty, a path we have to follow no matter where it may lead. Perhaps, if God so wishes, we'll survive and live out our years in peace. If not, we'll be united in heaven."

"Marcel, please," she begged.

"No, my dear, I must go. The men are waiting."

"I can't part with you like this," she cried.

"There's no other course. I'm a soldier. I don't have the right to break my oath, shed my duty. Nor do you!" He straightened up, adjusted his equipment and smiled at her. "I know how brave you are, Justine. Don't lose heart now."

She clung to him in a long farewell kiss. Then Marcel gently disengaged her arms and strode off to join the other men. She watched him through a film of tears until he turned a corner and was gone.

# 6

*L'Ecole du Sacré Coeur* had not been damaged during the punishing air raid because the German bombers had concentrated their attack on the dock area. When she saw the old building standing untouched, Justine hurried across the square with heightening relief. She skirted the place where Berthe had been killed; someone had covered the body with a blanket. Probably Father Gorot, she thought.

Justine paused outside the school for a moment. It would not do for the children to see her panting and shaken. She rearranged her uniform and pushed vagrant wisps of hair into place. At last, somewhat more composed, she squeezed between the sagging doors and entered the building.

No sound but her footsteps disturbed the silence. She heard no voice, no movement. Sudden fear sent a numbing shock through her. In contrast to the cheerful sunshine, the interior of the place was a gloomy, shadowed cavern filled with nameless terrors. She called out, but the only answer was her own voice echoing from a dozen dark recesses.

She dashed down the long corridor to the cellar. A candle flickered below, the tiny flame casting its wan and feeble glow in the overwhelming darkness.

"Father Gorot! Children! Where are you?"

Her words bounced off the walls and faded mockingly in the depths of that massive basement. Disregarding safety, Justine rushed pell-mell down the perilous staircase. She saw at once that the cellar was abandoned. Half-eaten food lay scattered about; a forgotten sweater was cast aside; the spluttering candle was the only proof that this refuge had been recently occupied. She wrung her hands in frenzied dismay. "They're gone! You've lost them! Gone! Gone! Gone!" an imaginary voice whispered accusingly in her ears.

She tried to think but her thoughts were disjointed, an unintelligible rush of confusion and dread. All at once, she noticed a piece of paper propped near the candle. It was a note written in a shaky scrawl. Holding it to the dim light, she read:

> Madame,
> Soldiers came with a truck. We wanted to wait for you, but they made us leave. We are going to a boat, they said. I asked to stay, but was refused permission. Bombs are falling. We do not know if you are alive. If you should see this, I swear I will stay with the children while I draw a breath. The little ones are calling for you.
>
> Father Ignatius Gorot.

She stared at the note for a long time, then crumpled and threw it away. Admiral Platon must have despatched a truck immediately, figuring the motorcycle would bring her to the school ahead of the big vehicle. The bomb that destroyed the *Adeleine* had upset his timing; but by then he could not recall the truck.

Father Gorot and the children were some place in flaming Dunkerque. How would she rejoin them? Justine trembled, crushed by despondency; she was trapped in a maze of tragic circumstance, a victim of overwhelming disaster.

She wanted to surrender, sink down here and not go on fighting. It made little difference whether she died in this unwholesome place or outside, buried under the ruins of the city. She looked at the waning candle. The dying flame seemed to symbolize the hopeless situation of Dunkerque, Belgium, the world. Soon it would be snuffed out and only darkness would remain.

But some small spark of resistance kept alive to rekindle her determination; to die was easy, very easy—it was only hard to strive, to endure, to live. Her despair was replaced by cold and unrelenting hatred of the Nazis. If she gave up now, it would be their victory and this she could not bear. They had not beaten her yet. Not while she lived and had the strength left to strike back, even in the most insignificant way.

For years she had thought of the children at *La Maison* as her own. A mother fought for her children until death. Justine thought of Marcel going back into the battle when it would have been simpler to walk out. For his sake, for hers and for the children's, she had to keep trying.

At that instant the candle flame burned out and she was in total darkness. She knew then that it would be impossible to cower in that pitch blackness like a frightened animal. She had pride and dignity, courage and purpose.

Feeling her way, Justine climbed the stairs and went out into the square. The glaring sun made her squint. Walking rapidly, she started for the center of the city, on the now familiar path. As she crossed a street an ambulance, marked with British colors, bounced toward her on the torn-up pavement. Justine jumped out into the middle of the road, waving her arms. The vehicle came to a skidding stop and the driver stuck his head out of the cab.

"You ruddy fool! Are you trying to get yourself killed! Lucky I saw you in time," he shouted. "Get out of my way, you flaming idiot!"

"Take me to the docks!" Justine cried in French.

"What are you jabbering about, woman? I don't understand a blinking word," the driver said.

The rear door of the ambulance opened and a young lieutenant, arm in a sling, stepped out of the vehicle.

In French he asked, "What is the trouble, madame?"

"I must get to the docks," she said.

"That's where we're supposed to go. But we went astray. Can you guide us? I have some badly wounded men in here. They're scheduled for evacuation to England."

"I know the way. May I help with the men? I'm a nurse."

"You're a godsend." He walked to the driver. "Tompkins, here's a bit of luck. This lady can show us to the docks."

"That's the first good news I've heard in a long time." Tompkins grinned.

As the officer translated, Justine described the route. Then she climbed into the back of the ambulance. There was little she could do for the six wounded men lying on stretchers, beyond checking their bandages.

"I fear for their lives if they are not hospitalized soon," she said, as the ambulance lurched away.

The officer grunted. "Poor lads. We were told a ship was ready to sail."

Justine did not tell him about the *Adeleine*. "Perhaps so. I hope you make it."

When they reached the docks, there was a long line of ambulances parked bumper to bumper. Walking wounded milled about aimlessly. Stretchers with wounded men blocked the sidewalk, the pier and reached on to the sandy beach. Hundreds were lying in the open; their moans made a dreadful noise. It was an unforgettable panorama of human agony.

A few doctors and some corpsmen passed among the stretchers, trying to ease the suffering. Someone had planted a huge Red Cross flag on a staff. The banner fluttered listlessly in the breeze. The *Adeleine,* still at her mooring, belched thick clouds of greasy smoke.

Two smaller ships were being towed by tugs to a pier opposite the burning vessel. Never in her life had Justine witnessed such mass suffering. She walked away from the ambulance staring incredulously at the injured men; this was a page out of Dante's *Inferno,* the ravings of tortured mankind.

A scout car cruised slowly up and down. In it sat an officer with a bullhorn. His hoarse voice announced in French and English: "Keep your places! We're bringing in ships. The loading will soon start. Stay calm."

Justine began her search for the children. She pushed through the crowds of waiting soldiers, losing heart each passing minute. Then she saw them, clustered in a group near the water's edge, their uniforms making a blotch of pale blue in the background of drab khaki battle dress.

With a glad cry, Justine pressed toward them and

at last was close enough to call out. *"Mes enfants!"* she cried above the babel of groaning. The children saw her and rushed to her. There were hugs and kisses and tears. Even Father Gorot wept without shame as soldiers watched curiously.

The joyful reunion tapered off into tedious, strained waiting. The two ships tied up and the slow work of boarding began. The stretchers were carried up the gangplanks with aggravating slowness and the throng thinned out sluggishly.

The hours passed and the sun was sinking in the west. The children were sitting or lying on the sand. Some of them had fallen asleep. Father Gorot, perched on a piece of driftwood, talked to Justine in low tones.

"It has been a miracle, this day," he said. "The *boche* airplanes never came back."

"A miracle," Justine agreed wearily, wondering where the Germans were.

They could not then know it, but the miracle was not a divine one. Admiral Platon had stormed, pleaded and cajoled for aerial protection to guard the evacuation of the wounded. For once the authorities in London and Paris responded effectively. Every available R.A.F. fighter and all the planes the French could muster were now flying on constant patrol. They had intercepted dozens of Nazi bombers miles from Dunkerque. With incredible bravery the men of the Allied air forces made an impenetrable shield that not a single enemy plane could penetrate.

The frustrated *Stukas* and *Heinkels* had turned against Calais and Boulogne, pouring tons of bombs on those cities—but that Sunday, May 19, Dunkerque was spared. The ship loading continued as dusk closed in. The first ship got underway. She moved clumsily out of the harbor, towed through the minefields by a tugboat.

The second vessel weighed anchor soon after. Meanwhile a small 900-ton Danish collier, the *Leika*, had nosed into a pier. The last litter cases were taken aboard her and columns of walking wounded began to shuffle aboard. The movement toward the ship reached the children. Justine awakened them and the youngsters stumbled along in the slow-moving mass.

It was dark by the time they reached the pierside and stood within reach of the gangplank. The *Leika's* decks were crowded. Men's faces loomed palely at the railing. Suddenly a British captain, carrying a hooded flashlight, bellowed, "That's all! Ship's loaded!"

A mass groan went up from those left on the dock. To Justine the announcement came like a death knell. With a cry she rushed to the officer and screamed, "No! No! You can't sail! I have fifty children waiting to go on board. They will surely die! Admiral Platon promised us a place!"

Rough hands seized her, but she wrestled free.

"Children! Can't you see? Children!" she shouted.

"What's she babbling about?" the officer asked.

"There's a whole pack of young ones back here, sir!" a soldier said. "They've been in line for hours!"

"Tell her we don't have any more room," the officer said.

Suddenly there was a shout from the ship. "Captain, hold it! We'll make room for them," a voice called.

After some commotion on the deck, men began stepping down the gangplank to the dock. A thick-shouldered sergeant, with a bandaged head, led them off. He saluted the captain and said, "Sir, these men volunteered to make way for the children."

"Volunteered?" the captain asked.

"Yes, sir. It's our war, not theirs. We'll take our chances."

The captain turned to Justine. "Do you understand? These men are giving up their places."

Justine did not understand the English, but she realized what was happening. Impulsively, she kissed the sergeant on the cheek.

"Blimey, ma'am," he stammered. "Blimey! It don't call for kissing."

"All right, all right, get those children aboard," the captain snapped.

A dozen men sprang forward to help. Within minutes the children of *La Maison* were on the *Leika*.

Father Gorot stood at the foot of the gangplank. Justine turned to him. "Are you coming, Father?" she asked.

"No, madame. My place is here," he said simply, and gently pushed her to the gangplank.

She trudged up slowly, not daring to look back at the men on the dock. And suddenly she remembered a quotation from the Bible: "Greater love hath no man than this, that a man lay down his life for his friends."

And that gave her hope for the future. Even amid this horror, there was still love. Humanity was not lost, for while love endured, hate could not long survive.

The *Leika* churned slowly away from her berth and swung around for the voyage to England, to safety. The night was dark; the way ahead uncharted. But at least there was hope.

# Author's Note

*The Long Escape* is based on a true story. Names have been changed, some situations dramatized and others enlarged for the purposes of the book. But the facts are true. The incidents were told to me by the woman I have called Justine Raymond; some of them were recounted in a fragmentary memoir which she wrote long after the ordeal of Dunkerque.

I have attempted to show that brave men and women are sometimes assailed by fear and doubt; courage is an intangible. He who is brave one moment, may be a coward the next. The saga of Justine Raymond is merely an incident in a terrible war; it is an epic that was repeated many times, but I do not know all those stories, I know only this one. If sudden death, horror and violence appear in this work, it is because war consists of such ugliness.

I do not think that young readers should be shielded from the sordid facets of recent history. I believe war has been glorified by popular media. Only by revealing the actual face of war can young people be made to realize how senseless it is; perhaps another generation will do better than mine did and bring an end to the abomination of war.

The events in this book happened to real people and some of the participants still reside in Belgium and elsewhere on the continent. It may please readers to know that my "Justine Raymond" is alive and well; that "Marcel" came through the war after nearly five years in the Belgian Resistance. "Raoul" joined the Resistance and lived until 1948.

The children of *La Maison* spent five years in England under the aegis of an international relief organization. All fifty returned to Belgium in 1945; some found their parents, some went to relatives, some were cared for by various agencies. Today they are grown men and women with children of their own.

In preparing this work, I had good help and advice. Mrs. Lenore Sorin was instrumental in gathering research material; several friends in England, who had fought at Dunkerque, provided me with factual background; the resources of the New-York Historical Society were placed at my disposal as were those of the Fifth Avenue Branch, New York Public Library.

My agent, Miss Candida Donadio, always had a cheery word. My wife was ever patient, gentle and kind. Mrs. Lee Levin conscientiously typed the manuscript from my cluttered and practically illegible script. And, of course, my son, Jack, curbed his nine-year-old ebullience during working hours.

I.W.

New York, November, 1963

## ABOUT THE AUTHOR

Irving Werstein was born in Brooklyn, graduated from high school in Richmond Hill, Long Island, and attended New York University. His early career was colorful and varied. It ranged from working in a radio factory to repairing dolls in a doll hospital. He was a summer comedian in the Catskills, a salesman, a camp counsellor, a straight actor.

But ever since he helped edit his high school newspaper, Irving Werstein wanted to write. He sold his first story in 1938. While serving in an infantry regiment from 1941 to 1945, he also worked as a staff correspondent for *Yank*. Now his published work includes numerous magazine stories, television and radio scripts, and an impressive list of books for young adults.

Mr. Werstein and his wife enjoy traveling and have lived in Mexico, Italy, England, Denmark, France and Holland. They have a young son and now make their home in New York City.

TR 5·30 - 7·10 pm

## DATE DUE